Loddiges of H

the largest hothouse in the world

David Solman

Additional research by Graham Douglas
Edited by Jane Straker

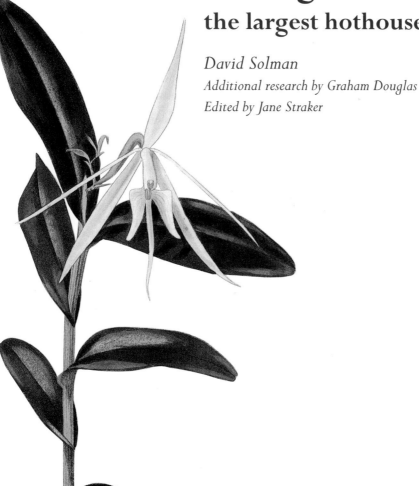

A HACKNEY SOCIETY PUBLICATION

THE HACKNEY SOCIETY was founded in 1969 to encourage by all possible means the improvement of the environment of the London Borough of Hackney, its buildings, streets and parks, as a pressure group made up of local residents. The Society is dependent on the help of volunteers. and the more people participate in its activities, the more effective it can be.

The Society meets monthly for a programme of walks and talks about the history and built environment of the Borough, and has published books and walks on that subject which are available from bookshops and local libraries.

For further information about the Society or its publications, please write to The Hackney Society at 115 Eleanor Road, London E8 1DN.

TITLE PAGE
Epidendrum nocturnum from The Botanical Cabinet *1817–33. Courtesy of the British Museum*

Published by The Hackney Society
Designed by Susan Clarke for
Expression Printers Ltd, London N5 1JT

ISBN 0–9506558 9 9

British Library Cataloguing in Publication Data
A catalogue record for this book is available from the British Library.

CONTENTS

TOP **Drimia undulata**
BELOW **Thermopsis
fabacea**
*Illustrations of plants at
Loddiges Nursery from*
The Botanical Cabinet
*published by C. Loddiges
& Sons, 1817–33*

FOREWORD

In this book David Solman has not only fulfilled his prime objective of giving us a superb account of, arguably, one of the most important and remarkable nurseries in the history of plant nurseries but he has also achieved far more – he has recorded in great detail, the history of Hackney over a period of about 70 years, drawing a vivid picture of the area, its people and their way of life. The rise to pre-eminence of Loddiges Nursery coincides, as one would expect, with the explosion in the discovery of plants. During the early years of the Paradise Field Nursery, Joseph Banks sailed with Cook, as official naturalist, on his journey to discover New Zealand and Australia (1768–71). Two years later Francis Mason was plant collecting in South Africa And it was he who was responsible for bringing back half of the known Pelargoniums, *Amaryllis* and the Bird of Paradise Flower, *Strelitzia reginae*, and many Cape Heaths. During the later great days of Loddiges the plant hunters Allan Cunningham (Australia) and David Douglas (North America) were multiplying the numbers of plants that were becoming available in Britain.

By reading this book we begin to get a real sense of the way all the elements of gardening, plant collecting and nursery work dovetailed together. This is a history not only of one nursery but of how Britain became the pre-eminent gardening country of the world.

Roger Phillips

Veronica perfoliata
from The Botanical
Cabinet *1817–33.*
Courtesy of the
British Museum

ACKNOWLEDGEMENTS

The author would like to thank Graham Douglas for joint research into many areas discussed in this book and in particular for original historical research on the location of Busch and Loddiges' nursery, their overseas contacts and suppliers. Much of this has been jointly published by the author and Graham Douglas in the 'Friends of Hackney Archives' magazine, *The Terrier*. In addition, thanks are due to the following for generous help:

Family tree: Marjorie Loddiges

Information about Silvester's garden: Isobel Watson

Information about Bartram, Busch and late eighteenth-century Russian gardens: Professor Anthony Cross of Cambridge University, Marcus Kohler of Berlin, and staff at Historic Bartram's Garden, Pennsylvania.

Information about Adelaide Botanic Garden: Barbara Best.

For encouragement to prepare the research for publication, thanks are due to Jane Straker of the Hackney Society. Thanks are due to Nick Arnold for editorial comments on the manuscript, to Karen Parker for picture research, to John Riethmüller for proof reading, to the Royal Horticultural Society for generously assisting with the pictures, and to the numerous libraries, archives and institutions in Britain and abroad who have so helpfully responded to requests for information.

Special thanks are due to David Mander of Hackney Archives Department for access to documents, and to Isobel Watson of the Friends of Hackney Archives for encouragement to publish the author's research into Hackney's horticulturalists and naturalists in *The Terrier*.

🌿 Introduction to Loddiges Nursery

The environs of Hackney Town Hall cover the site of what was once the foremost nursery garden in London. Here was a latter-day Eden where scenes reminiscent of a rain forest were created inside the largest hothouse in the world, and where exotic plants, which in nature lived in different parts of the globe, grew side by side.

The Nursery was also a leading grower of rare American plants, and was noted for its vast range of temperate trees and shrubs. In its grounds on Mare Street it laid out an early tree collection which was for many years the largest named collection in the world. Its arousal of the Victorian passion for growing ferns, particularly inside ornate Wardian Cases, and for encouraging the flowering of tropical orchids, were but two of its further claims to fame.

Whilst some members of the family were engaged in the learned scientific societies of the time, others managed the day-to-day business. The family was instrumental in founding the Royal Microscopical Society, and experimenting with new methods of plant packaging which enabled the successful introduction of tea- and quinine- producing plants in India and rubber in Malaya. Horticulture and science seemed to run in the blood of successive generations of the Loddiges family.

During the Nursery's heyday the Loddiges' influence extended beyond the shores of Britain, leaving its mark as far afield as the imperial gardens of St Petersburg and the Adelaide Botanic Garden.

It is perhaps inevitable that all empires decay, and so it was with Loddiges Nursery. The once flourishing family business finally closed its gates to the Victorian world in 1852. But the final chapter of its history was to be written two years later when Londoners witnessed the stately cortège of thirty-two plumed horses as they drew a giant palm tree, the botanic gem of the Loddiges Nursery, to its final resting place at the Crystal Palace at Sydenham.

Although the Nursery itself has long since disappeared under nineteenth- and twentieth-century bricks and mortar, surviving trees from its arboretum still grow in Abney Park Cemetery, a mile and a half to the north. In the woodlands of this impressive garden cemetery, now an inner-city local nature reserve, some of Loddiges' trees have self-sown or *naturalised*, adding colour and interest to the setting of the Loddiges family vaults.

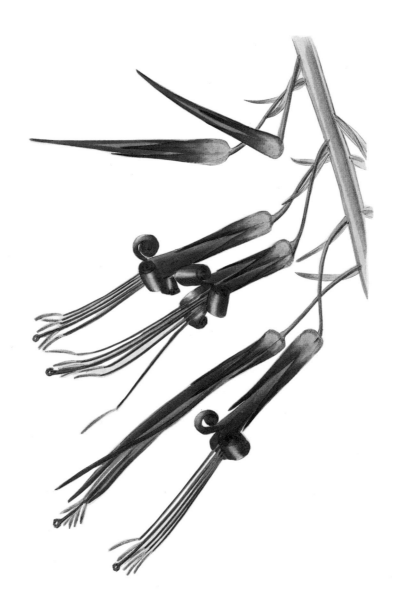

Pitcairnia staminea
from The Botanical
Cabinet *1817–33.*
Courtesy of the
British Museum

CHAPTER ONE
❧ The origins and early years of Loddiges Nursery

Loddiges Nursery became 'the greatest of the nurseries dealing in rare exotics'[1], and 'London's leading nurserymen for the first four decades of the nineteenth century'.[2] The seeds of their success were sown by one German émigré, Johann Busch, 1730/1–95, and their remarkable development nurtured by another, Joachim Conrad Loddiges, 1738–1826. Their achievements were assisted, and perhaps surpassed, by the endeavours of Joachim Conrad's two sons, George and William, who married into the local Methodist community, and linked the nursery with the scientific societies of the period.

John Busch: founder of the Nursery

Johann Busch, anglicised to John Busch or John Bush, was a native of Hanover in Germany who came to England in the early 1740s. Historians are not certain when Busch settled in Hackney. By 1756 he was recorded as living in the parish of St John, renting land on Mare Street to establish a small plant nursery.[3]

Apart from introducing the Marsh Rosemary *Ledum palustre* into Britain in the 1760s, surprisingly little is known about Busch's nursery.[4] However, it appears to have built-up an influential clientele. Documents in the Royal Archives list Busch as a supplier of unusual plants to the private botanical garden of Princess Augusta, whose plant collection forms the basis of The Royal Botanic Gardens, Kew.[5] Foreign clients included Baron Friedrich August von Veltheim and Otto von Münchausen. Much of this business arose from Busch's links with Peter Collinson of Mill Hill, Middlesex, through whom he obtained seeds from all over the world. Seeds came from St Petersburg, by 'the Caravan' from the Jesuits in China, from Siberia, and from North America.

Collinson was financier to the famous Quaker seed collector, John Bartram of Philadelphia and distributed 'Bartram's Boxes' to a select list of clients, including John Busch. Accompanying some of the seeds were preserved specimens of the plants. These were sent by Collinson to Carl Linnaeus to be given botanical names. 'Bartram's Boxes', otherwise known as 'Quaker Seeds', were all the more valuable for this; their contents could be grown by specialist nurseries such as Busch's, and the rarities sold to collectors for high prices, once they were scientifically named.

Before 1743, John Bartram's work was partly financed by Peter Collinson's friend, Robert James, 8th Earl Petre of Thorndon Hall, Essex. He was the foremost collector of American trees and shrubs in England, and his untimely death in 1743, at the age of thirty, led to the auctioning of 220,000 specimens. Many went to Woburn and Goodwood, but Collinson distributed others to nurserymen. It has been suggested that John

Busch, arriving in England at this date, may have purchased part of the collection in order to establish himself as a supplier of rare American plants to German gardens. However his work in these early years in England remains unresearched.

> *From John Busch*
> *London 8 June 1764*
>
> *Sir,*
> *The last three boxes of seeds proved not to expectation so that in one of them there were but eight sorts of seeds in the whole box, ye other not above half full. My friends in Germany are not willing to pay me the full price for them but I am in hopes I shall get payed for two boxes, for which I shall be accountable for.*
> *As to this year's boxes, I have had no complaints for which I shall make my payment good for them to Mr. Collinson.*
> *Please to send me 3 boxes next year, 1765, that is 2 boxes of the large forest kind and no shrubby kinds mixt with them, and one box of the common, with all the kinds of seeds. With so douing you will oblige.*
> *Your Humble Servant*
> *John Busch*

Letter from John Busch to the famous Quaker seed collector John Bartram in Philadelphia (sent via Peter Collinson of Mill Hill, Middlesex, Bartram's financier, distributor and fellow Quaker botanist).[6]

At the end of this letter, Collinson added his own comment to John Bartram: 'I don't know what to do with these Germans. Some of the boxes was open'd & plundered by the Spaniard. One of Gordon's I saw was so, possibly these might be so too.'

John Busch in Russia 1771-89

In 1771 John Busch was enticed abroad, not as a supplier of rare seeds and plants, but as an Imperial Head Gardener and landscape architect. He was commissioned by Catherine the Great to lay out one of the earliest examples in Russia of landscaping in the 'English-style'.

Empress Catherine was a great enthusiast for the new naturalistic garden style which had been pioneered in England by 'Capability' Brown.[8] Since her accession in 1762, she had been determined to replace Peter the Great's formal Dutch-style gardens with their fish canals, straight paths, clipped and espalier trees, shady walks and untrained trees.[9] In the year following Busch's arrival, she enthused to Voltaire: 'I love to distraction those gardens in the English style – their curving lines, the gentle slopes, the ponds like lakes. My Anglomania predominates over my plantomania.'[10]

Such was Catherine's enthusiasm that Russian gardeners and architects were sent to England to learn the art at first hand. An imperial gardener Andrei Ekleben and three assistants arrived in May 1769, and the architect Vasilli Ivanovich Neyelov arrived in 1771. Through her ambassador in London, Count Czernichew, in 1769 she secured the services of the Scot Charles Sparrow, and in the following year turned down a recommendation from 'Capability' Brown to employ Thomas Cloase of Hampton Court, selecting John Busch instead. He was ideal, since Catherine, who had been born in Germany, could communicate with him in her native language and explain pre-

The 'English-style' of gardening spreads to Russia

An edict of 1762 had enabled Russian aristocrats to travel abroad. The end of the Seven Years War in Europe in 1763 made it easier for them to travel to Britain. Amongst the first to report back was Ivan Shavalov, who enthused others with his interest in 'English-style' gardening. In 1764 he wrote 'The whole art is being close to nature. I think it is the best way'.

A few years later Vladimir Orlov, Director of the Academy of Sciences, studied the concept. He wrote 'In their design the attempt is made to imitate nature and conceal the work that is necessary and frequently greater than in regular gardens; in these gardens everything is spread around — here a wood, here a shrubbery, here flowers, here a pond'.

A particularly influential visitor was Princess Ekaterina Dashkova who had been involved in the court revolution which had put Catherine on the throne, and later became Director of the Academy of Sciences. She visited England in October 1770 and found the gardens to be 'worthy of being described by a writer of epics'.[7]

Tsarskoe Selo Park in the late 1700s when Busch had completed its landscaping and still resided here. From P. Polevoi, Istoriia Slovesnosii 1900

cisely what she wanted to achieve.

Busch was initially assigned to the gardens at Kolomenskoe, an imperial residence under construction near Moscow. A year later he is believed to have helped Charles Sparrow at Gatchina as well as landscaping a pleasure ground at Pulkovo, half way between Tsarskoe Selo and St Petersburg. The official court journal records Catherine's visit here in May 1774. The Empress was evidently delighted. On entering the garden, and seeing a winding shady gravel walk planted on both sides, she appeared struck with surprise, and exclaimed: 'This is what I wanted!' This walk led to a fine lawn, with gravel walks around it, which seemed to strike her still more forcibly and she again said: 'This is what I have long wished to have!'[11]

The following year, Busch was promoted to Imperial Head Gardener at Tsarskoe Selo, the Empress' summer palace, south of St Petersburg.[12] Here, in return for an annual salary of 19,000 roubles, he created the 'English-style' landscape which had for so long been desired by Catherine, and built a range of hothouses to grow exotic fruit. He was assisted after 1780 by a Scot named John McLaren, and every summer by between 60 and 70 serfs.[13]

At Tsarskoe Selo, Busch, his wife, daughters and son Joseph, lived in a flat above the orangery.[14] In 1781 the diarist Elizabeth Dimsdale visited the family. Elizabeth was the third wife of Dr Thomas Dimsdale, the Quaker physician who inoculated the Empress against smallpox.[15]

Ekaterinsky Park

The town of Tsarskoe Selo ('Tsar's Village') was renamed Detskoe Selo ('Children's Village') after the revolution in 1918. In 1937, a century after the death of Russia's greatest poet, it was named Pushkin. He had spent his formative years at a school next to the Ekaterinsky Palace, to the south and west of which lies Ekaterinsky Park, the landscape laid out by John Busch and decorated by the architecture of his son-in-law Charles Cameron, and by Vasilli Neyelov. The parks of Tsarskoe Selo made a considerable impression on Pushkin, and are widely reflected in his poetry.

Elizabeth had been acquainted with John Busch in England and renewed her friendship whilst staying at the palace as a guest of the Empress. Elizabeth Dimsdale regularly visited Busch and relied on his knowledge of Russian ways for parts of her diary. As she discussed the abject condition of the Russian serf with Busch, she noted approvingly that:

> the gardens are laid out in the English taste and are very prettily diversified with lawns, gravel walks, and a wood, a very fine large piece of water is near the centre with an island.[16]

Another of John Busch's distinguished visitors was Charles Cameron (c.1742–1812), Architect to the Court of Russia.[17] Many of Cameron's fine buildings still stand. They were wrecked during the Second World War, but have since been painstakingly restored by the Communist authorities. Cameron's chief architectural achievements were the Palace of Tsarskoe Selo and the later Palace of Pavlovsk. Cameron, though primarily an architect, was also required to landscape the grounds of Pavlovsk; indeed the first results of his work appeared in the park. It has long been disputed how he achieved this, and who helped him, since Pavlovsk Park was, and still is said to be 'the most beautiful in Russia'.[18] It is possible that Charles Cameron and John Busch worked together closely on landscape projects, since one of John Busch's daughters, Catherine, married Cameron and remained in Russia with him.[19]

John Busch's son, Joseph Busch (1760–1838) also stayed on, succeeding his father as Imperial Head Gardener on his father's departure for

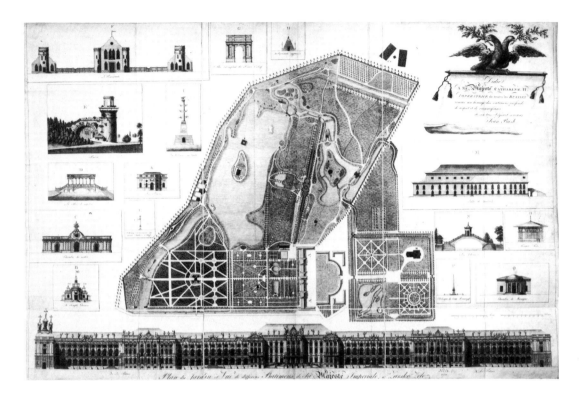

Plan of the Gardens of Tsarskoe Selo c.1790s by Joseph Busch. Courtesy of the British Museum

England in 1789. The hand-over was marked by the presentation to Catherine of a plan of the 'English-style' gardens drawn by Joseph Busch. Seven years later Empress Catherine died. Her successor required him to be more cost-conscious, and in 1810 Joseph Busch left to lay out an 'English-style' garden on Elagin Island in the Neva Delta around Carlo Rossi's Palace.[20]

Ten years later Joseph Busch was still employed in imperial service and published a paper through the Horticultural Society of London on his training of fruit trees: 'Observations on a Method of Training Apple Trees in Russia to Preserve

Charles & Catherine Cameron

*C*harles Cameron (c.1742–1812) emigrated to Russia in 1779, passing himself off as a Scottish Jacobite, although even his wife may never have discovered his imposture. His death in spring 1812 was reported to the Tsar on 16 April 1812.[22] Charles Cameron left no fortune and no children and his library and effects were sold in November 1812 through Jean Grabit, 78 Nevsky Prospekt, St Petersburg. A copy of the 210 page catalogue is preserved in Moscow.

Following her husband's death, Catherine Cameron, née Catherine Busch, was granted a pension of 1,500 roubles per annum by Emperor Alexander. Four years later, with failing health she prepared to return to England. The Emperor generously informed her that she would continue to receive the pension, but she died in 1817, shortly before making the return journey.

them from Frost during Winter'.[21] Some time thereafter he retired to England.

The Hackney Nursery whilst John Busch was in Russia 1771-89

The Russian commission took John Busch eighteen years to complete, from 1771 to 1789. Whilst abroad he left his Hackney nursery and its overseas correspondents in the capable hands of his fellow German émigré, Joachim Conrad Loddiges.

The precise arrangements between them remain unclear, but it is known that Joachim Conrad purchased all or some of the rights to supply Busch's distinguished list of clients. Most importantly, Loddiges acquired the rights to receive exotic seeds from Busch's overseas correspondents, particularly from John Bartram, whose business passed after his death in 1777 to his son William.

Other correspondents included professional collectors and amateur enthusiasts in overseas government, religious and military service. Through such correspondents, Busch's Nursery, and after 1771, Loddiges Nursery, encouraged plant exploration throughout the world. The exotic seeds, often of hitherto unknown plants, were in themselves worth little, but in the hands of an expert gardener they could grow into plants of great value, especially if they were the first of their kind to flower in Britain or Germany.

Joachim Conrad Loddiges could only afford £100 to buy Busch's seed business in 1771; this amounted to his entire life savings, built up over his years as gardener to Dr Silvester.[23] Perhaps it was sufficient to buy only the key parts of the business. It is known that Busch continued to hold the tenancy of, and to be recorded as liable for rent on nursery land in or near to Mare Street after his departure to Russia in 1771.

One of the sites which Busch continued to rent whilst abroad, was owned, or more probably managed, by Jeremiah Bentham, father of the Utilitarian philosopher Jeremy Bentham who later founded University College, London. On 31 December 1779, Jeremiah and Jeremy Bentham wrote to Samuel Bentham, Jeremy's brother, and included in their discussion of Samuel's forthcoming trip to St Petersburg a mention of the family connection with Busch:

> When you arrive there don't forget my tenant Busch, Her Majesty's head gardener, and let him know, I shall continue his name as my tenant in the receipts I give to his substitute Loddiges, at Hackney.[24]

It is possible that this land lay to the south-east of Mare Street on the Cass Estate, since the Cass Trustees' legal advisor was Jeremiah Bentham.[25]

John Busch & Joseph Busch: the later years

On his return to England in 1789, John Busch settled at Busch House, Isleworth, at the north-west corner of the Duke of Northumberland's Syon Park estate. The house still stands and is used as a school. It lies between 'Busch Corner'

Isleworth Church in 1795, the year of John Busch's burial

and the main entrance to Syon Park. John Busch lived here for the final six years of his life and is buried nearby at Isleworth Church. Before the church was destroyed by fire in 1943, a plaque read:

> In memory of John Busch, late of Isleworth. He migrated (about 1744) from Svege, Lüneborg, Hanover, to St John's Parish, Hackney; and in the service of H.I.M. Catherine II laid out the parks of … Tsarskoe Selo etc. Also of his son Jos. Ch. Busch who in the same service (1778–1833) reclaimed Yslagin Island, St Petersburg etc. Placed by desire of Jos. London Busch (1812–95) son of the last named of Chichester, by his only child, Arthur Pitt Busch.

At Isleworth John Busch continued to work as

an amateur or professional nurseryman, introducing the Grey Alder tree *Alnus incana* into Britain, along with several shrubs including a flowering currant and a rhododendron species.[26] John Busch continued to have property interests in Hackney since land near Graham Road, off Mare Street, did not leave the Busch family's possession until John Busch's son Joseph surrendered its lease in 1815.[27]

Joseph Busch maintained a clear link with Loddiges Nursery, for he acted as a correspondent for the firm, supplying rare seeds and plants. This was rewarded by Joachim Conrad Loddiges' son George, who in 1830 named the beautiful Siberian lily *Lilium buschianum* in honour of Joseph Busch. Joseph had supplied this magnificent plant to Loddiges Nursery before it had been scientifically described:

> We received this in 1829 from our valued friend Mr Joseph Busch, of St Petersburg: as we consider it an entire new species, we could not do better than name it after him, especially as we are not aware that any plant has ever been dedicated to him, although he has contributed much to the advancement of botanical science, and has sent many new plants from time to time to this country.[28]

This hardy and fragrant lily was illustrated in full colour as plate 1628 in Loddiges' publication *The Botanical Cabinet*.

*Busch's Lily **Lilium bushianum***
Named by Joachim Conrad Loddiges in honour of Joseph Busch.
Illustration from The Botanical Cabinet *published by C. Loddiges & Sons 1817–33. Courtesy of the British Museum*

The location of Busch's nursery (1755/6-71)

It is likely that the 'Busch Nursery', such as it was, was no more than an assortment of scattered fields along Mare Street, perhaps rented on temporary terms. Busch never consolidated his growing plots around one prime site, as Joachim Conrad Loddiges was able to do after 1795/6, with attendant success.

What little we know of Busch's nursery indicates that it consisted of several small grounds, principally on the west side of Mare Street.[29] It was here that Busch was first recorded in the Poor Rate ledger in 1756 and where, in the following year, he paid a Church Rate on a field which was previously held by Thomas Pells.

By 1764 Busch was paying a Poor Rate on 'land late Thomas' in addition to his previous site, and although not charged Land Tax, he was listed as the landholder of 'an orchard behind Collins house in Mare Street, late Rebello'. By 1769–70 other fields (Mr Newton's and Mr Pearce's) had been acquired. The orchard was the one piece of land for which Busch was consistently liable for tax throughout this period.

The forms of tenure of Busch's nursery fields are not known, but Busch was never directly liable for more than three sites at a time when assessed on three different dates in 1770 for Land Tax, Poor Rate, and Highway Rate.

There is no explicit reference in the Hackney Land Tax and rate records of any direct transfer of land from Busch to Loddiges in 1771. This suggests that Joachim Conrad Loddiges may initially have acted as an agent for Busch, managing and disposing of his small plots, or renting them, but not immediately acquiring their leases. With respect to the land leased from Bentham, Joachim Conrad was described as Busch's 'substitute', suggesting that the lease had not been formally purchased and re-assigned although the land was effectively rented by Loddiges from Bentham. Practices of sub-leasing and under-letting on estate lands in Hackney became highly complex during this period and patterns of tenure and use are difficult to establish. Although we know that Joachim Conrad Loddiges acquired title to Busch's correspondents and clients, and no doubt his nursery stocks, his initial land tenure arrangements remain unclear.[30]

The early life of Joachim Conrad Loddiges

The early career of Joachim Conrad Loddiges has been neglected by historians. This is somewhat surprising, given the esteem in which Joachim Conrad was clearly held by both contemporaries and successors. Yet previous biographers have even been uncertain as to whether he came from Germany or the Low Countries.[31]

It has become clear that Joachim Conrad Loddiges was baptised in Hertzberg on 9 October 1738 and lived in his youth at Vrisbergholtzen in Hildesheim, Hanover. His father Caspar Burchart Loddiges was a nobleman's gardener. His grandfather had worked in Hanover as a gardener to the local Electors, who, from 1714, were also Kings of England.[32]

HACKNEY IN THE 1740s
(extract from a map by John Roque surveyed 1742–4)

*I*n 1756 the German émigré John Busch leased land in Hackney to begin his plant nursery. His catalogue from 1760 survives in Germany in the Harbeke Archive. From his small fields in Hackney and through his contact with the specialist American seed importer Peter Collinson, his catalogue 'aimed to provide most of the plants listed in Miller's Dictionary'. After 1758 the Nursery became a key intermediary in the supply of seeds and plants to German gardens. As Busch explained to Baron Veltheim 'I intend to sow and plant all Germany from England and North America'. Besides his Nursery, John Busch developed his interest in English-style gardening, showing touring German nobility the great gardens of England, and being sent German court gardeners to train.

1 John Busch's Orchard
(Rebello's Orchard at the date of this map)
Busch leased this land from Nathaniel Acton Lee in 1764. Its rates were paid by Joachim Conrad Loddiges after 1776.

2 The Cass Estate
Busch held land from Bentham who may have been acting for the Cass Estate.

3, 4 and 5 Land and shop later acquired by Joachim Conrad Loddiges.
3 Seven Acre Field
4 Bannister Lane
5 London Lane / Church Street shop

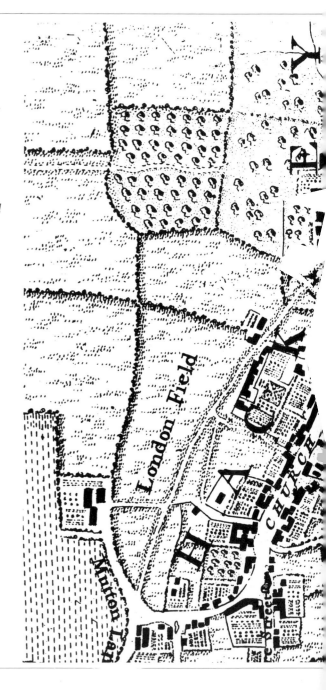

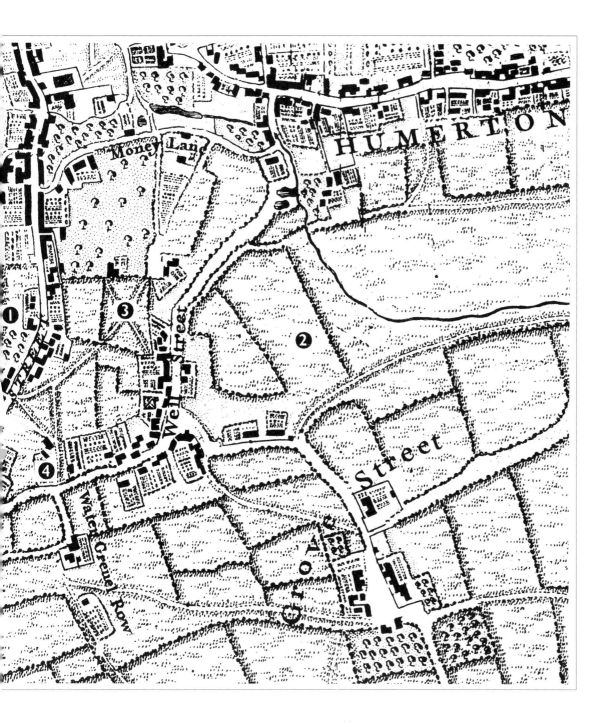

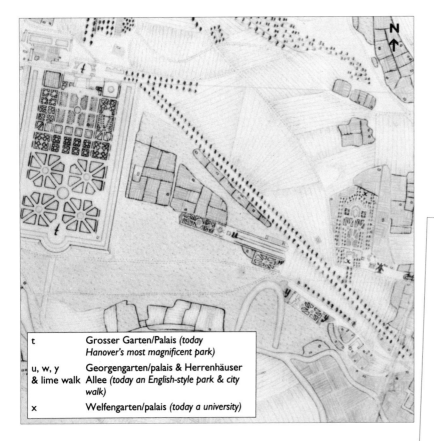

t	Grosser Garten/Palais (today Hanover's most magnificent park)
u, w, y & lime walk	Georgengarten/palais & Herrenhäuser Allee (today an English-style park & city walk)
x	Welfengarten/palais (today a university)

permit is one of the few surviving documents to mention Joseph Conrad Loddiges.[33] It describes Joachim Conrad Lochlies (sic) as a gardener at Hildesheim, authorised to travel to Haarlem in the Low Countries via Paderborn and Münster, and return thereafter back to Hildesheim.[34]

It seems likely that Joachim Conrad Loddiges took this journey in the hope of extending it to England, for with him he carried the apprenticeship testimonial provided by Joseph Conrad

Extract from plan of Hanover c.1760, showing the Royal Gardens of Herrenhäusen, north-west of the old city walls. Courtesy of the British Museum

Travels in the Low Country

At about the age of 16, Joachim Conrad Loddiges was apprenticed to the court and kitchen gardener, Joseph Conrad Weffer. After three years he gained an elaborate apprenticeship testimonial. He decided to travel to the Low Countries, a journey which, during The Seven Years War, required a travel permit. This was authorised by a commander in the Duc de Richelieu's Army on 26 January 1758. The

---

VINCENT JUDES de St PERN, Lieutenant General of the King's Army, Inspector General of the Infantry, Commandant of the French Grenadier Corps, Commandeur of the Royal Military Order of St Louis and Sub-Commander of the Orders of the Mr le Marechal Duke of Richelieu within the bishopric of Hildesheim.

We instruct those over whom our power extends, and we request others, to allow free passage of the said Joachim Conrad Lochlies*, gardener, to Haarlem, via Paderborn and Münster, without making any detour, and to return to Hildesheim, without giving him any hindrance, and on the contrary, giving him help and assistance.

Made 26 January 1758 at Hildesheim.

(* spelling as on the original French document)

Translation of travel permit authorised during The Seven Years War

Weffer, embellished with its large letterhead in the name of 'George II, King of England, France, Ireland and Duke of Brunswick'.[35]

Joachim Conrad Loddiges' stay in Velzen near Haarlem between 1758 and 1761 was a valuable staging post, a preparation for his career as a gardener in England. The area was noted for the large country residences of wealthy Amsterdam citizens, and employment here should not have

---

Translation of apprenticeship testimonial (1754–7) for Joachim Conrad Loddiges.[36] *Photograph courtesy of Hackney Archives Department*

His most illustrious
Highness High and Mighty Sovereign George, the King of Great Britain, France and Ireland, Protector of the Faith, Duke of Brunswick and Lüneburg, Treasurer and Elector of the Holy Roman Empire.

I, Joseph Conrad Weffer
at the current time appointed court and kitchen gardener, herewith announce and declare that this

Joachim Conrad Loddiges, native of Vrisbergholtzen in the parish of Hildesheim, son of Caspar Burchart Loddiges esquire, appointed gardener, has in this royal garden learned the nursery craft in three years under my instruction as from the first of July 1754 until 1757; also in these apprenticeship years he has shown himself as loyal, industrious, and patiently persevering as befits a God-fearing apprentice. I have also been fully satisfied with him. Meanwhile he intends to seek, after the completed apprenticeship, his fortune elsewhere, and to more perfect himself in his chosen vocation, and to this end he has requested of me a testimonial of his completed apprenticeship. This I have wanted to give him. It is therefore meant for all, and in particular those who are devoted to this laudable art/craft, who may seek and request, in a friendly manner, my service, if there is a want that the aforesaid Joachim Conrad Loddiges not only be recommended in every way, but also to be assisted in all possible ways. Such affection he has not only returned with loyal service and gratefulness, but I also am willing, according to the custom, to assist in returning the favour. To certify this I have signed this letter of apprenticeship myself, and verified it with my personal seal as it is at the royal kitchen garden of Hanover. The first of July in the Year One Thousand Seven Hundred and Fifty-seven.

Velzen, Harlem, 1700s A district well-known for its country estate gardens owned by the wealthy of Amsterdam where Joachim Conrad Loddiges gained employment 1758–61, and was introduced to Dr Silvester

Joachim Conrad Loddiges' arrival in Hackney

Dr Silvester's Gardener (1761-71)

Whilst employed at Velzen, Joachim Conrad Loddiges was introduced to the family of Dr (later Sir) John Baptist Silvester. The Silvester family was noted for its connections with the Low Countries and for its scientific interests.[38] Around 1760, Dr Silvester acquired a fine house with landscaped grounds near Mare Street, Hackney and invited Joachim Conrad to take charge of the gardens. In 1761 Silvester introduced Loddiges into this country as his gardener, employing him to re-landscape the grounds in a less formal style, and add a collection of 'foreign shrubs'.[39]

Dr Silvester's house and grounds are well-documented. The land ran south from the Hackney Brook and Pigwell Water behind the Mermaid Tavern on the west side of Mare Street, to below Silvester Road (where Silvester built five houses), ending west of the Spurstowe's almshouses. In the nineteenth century the grounds which had once been Silvester's were dissected by the railway; the old house lay north of Hackney Central Station, but its gardens lay chiefly to the south, centred upon Graham Road.

In 1777 Dr Silvester moved away from Hackney, retaining only his new Silvester Road houses as an investment. In the sale catalogue the gardens which Joachim Conrad Loddiges had laid out between 1762 and 1771 were a key feature:

In the Gardens, which are delicately laid out, and abound with the best of fruits &c, are two

been difficult for such a well-trained gardener. Here Joachim Conrad developed such a fluency in Dutch that some of his English biographers mistook him for a native of that country.[37]

Greenhouses, a Fruiting-house, and Succession-house. A curious Grotto, with a constant Stream murmuring through, replenishing a Canal well-stored with Fish; and at the entrance thereof a Willow of magnitude, with extending branches, affording a refreshing Shade. A Farm-yard with Barn, Stable, Cowhouse &c and 15 acres of land in high manurage; running through the centre thereof a Brook making five falls, the last in clamorous murmur; a Gothic Hermitage faces this cascade; which with ease may be converted into a Cold Bath. A Shrubby and Serpentine Walk (with flowering shrubs) nearly encompass the whole.[40]

Introduction of the common mauve rhododendron

Rhododendrons and azaleas, which belong to the same botanical genus but are treated separately by gardeners, were mainly introduced into cultivation in Britain during the nineteenth century from the Himalayas and Western China. However, seed of our most common species, the mauve rhododendron *Rhododendron ponticum*, came from Turkey, and had been introduced much earlier. It was grown successfully in the 1760s at Dr Silvester's garden. Joachim Conrad may have brought the seeds with him when he left Velzen in 1761. As these grew he became the first to supply and distribute young plants, having 'sold the first plant to the Marquis of Rockingham, a noble encourager of botany and gardening' in about 1763.[41]

By late Victorian times rhododendrons of all sorts had become popular evergreen shrubs. In *The Amateur's Flower Garden* (1871) Shirley Hibberd wrote that 'the money spent on rhododendrons during twenty years in this country would nearly suffice to pay off the National Debt'.[42]

From about 1800 onwards, the species introduced by Joachim Conrad Loddiges began to be widely used for underplanting woodlands on country estates. Today this popular shrub is blamed by conservationists for having invasively naturalised in valuable remnant woodlands and damp valleys throughout much of Britain, at the expense of the native flora. In Snowdonia National Park it has become a major issue in nature conservation.[43] Standing at Hackney Central Station, it is salutory to remember that here at Dr Silvester's garden, where seeds were first grown to add beauty to our gardens, their uncontrolled spread has since caused ecological damage in the countryside.

Loddiges' early Nursery (1771-86)

On 2 January 1770 Joachim Conrad Loddiges wrote to Dr Silvester, asking for advice on setting up his own business.[44] Perhaps Joachim Conrad had been encouraged by his success in selling rhododendrons, or perhaps a change in his personal circumstances had prompted a wish for greater independence. Just four weeks earlier he had married Sarah Aldous, and she was already carrying their child.[45]

The following year, John Busch's departure for Russia provided Joachim Conrad with what seemed an ideal opportunity. Although the detailed arrangements with Busch are unclear, and it is not known whether Dr Silvester was a party, by 1774 Loddiges had become a lease-holder in Mare Street.[46] Here he had a seed shop and nearby, a small nursery. An unpublished account records:

> Mr Conrad Loddiges first lived at the corner of London Lane (he lived there in 1775–6). He kept a seed shop, he had a small nursery at the back of St Thomas' Place (called at that time Bannister Lane).[47]

In 1777, Joachim Conrad Loddiges' former employer, Dr John Silvester, sold his house and

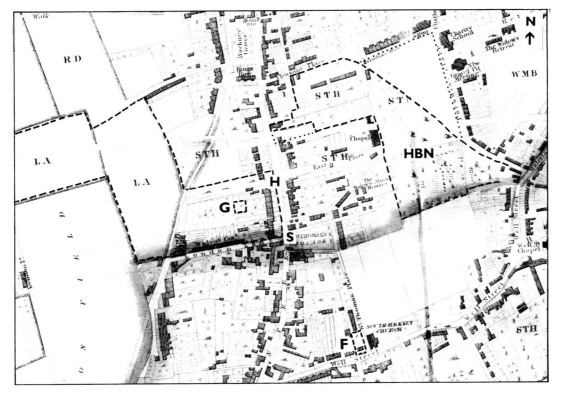

grounds and moved away from Hackney. In the same year, the Nursery financed the printing and publishing of its first and quite remarkable nursery catalogue. There were only two other printed trade lists at this date which used the scientific names of plants. Joachim Conrad went one step further than both by publishing the first-ever tri-lingual version, written in German, English and Latin.[48] Thereafter, printed catalogues became a distinctive feature of the business. As the Nursery's trade with continental Europe increased, some editions also included an introduction written in French.[49]

By 1778, Loddiges Nursery held three leases in Mare Street, including the seed shop and the site behind St Thomas' Place in Bannister Lane, off Well Street.[50] After 1781 the Land Tax records include information on landlords as well as lessees. For the first time we learn the names of Loddiges' three landlords:

- Bannister was landlord over the small field in Bannister Lane, sub-leased from St Thomas' Hospital.
- Sir Richard Hearne (syn. Heron) was landlord over a garden in Mare Street probably sub-

leased from Nathaniel Acton Lee. Nathaniel Acton Lee was landlord over Loddiges' seed shop and house and the associated land north of the corner of London Lane/Mare Street and south of the Horse and Groom.[51] This land included the small orchard which John Busch had acquired from Mr Rebello in 1764.

After about fifteen years or so as a leaseholder, the 47-year-old Joachim Conrad Loddiges was at last in a position to acquire his own freehold — the gardens and premises of an old house called Barbers Barn on the east side of Mare Street. During 1785 and 1786 unexpired leases on two adjacent fields, the property of St Thomas' Hospital became available. Joachim Conrad Loddiges acquired both. These were called Seven Acre Field (Paradise Field) and Church Street Field.[52]

The purchase of this land combined to give Joachim Conrad a sizeable increase in acreage. It offered a well-placed entrance onto the main thoroughfare, with ample scope for nursery outbuildings and greenhouses and the potential for income from property development. The tenanted part of the site, half of one of the two fields, continued to be let whilst Joachim Conrad moved his stock to the remaining area and set about disposing of his former scattered grounds.[53]

In 1787 the southern triangular half of Paradise Field was walled in, defining and securing the perimeter of Loddiges Nursery.[54] The boundary was retained until about 1820 when a southerly extension was made to accommodate an arboretum.[55]

LEFT *Photograph taken in 1994 of buildings on the site of Joachim Conrad's seed shop (corner of London Lane and Mare Street).*
RIGHT *Photograph, taken in 1994, of St Thomas' Place, Hackney, formerly Bannister Lane. The site of part of Joachim Conrad Loddiges' Nursery in the 1770s*

CHAPTER TWO
Loddiges' Paradise Field Nursery (1787-1816)

Although it achieved its greatest fame between the 1820s and 1840s the Nursery built up its important network of overseas correspondents during its earlier years at Paradise Field. In the Herbarium Library at Kew is a list drawn up by William Loddiges, giving the names of 151 plants which the Nursery introduced into general cultivation in Britain between 1782 and 1806. These included the aromatic Siberian Gentian *Gentiana decumbens* and the Nursery's speciality – Cape Heaths.

As Joachim Conrad Loddiges grew older, his

Hackney c.1795

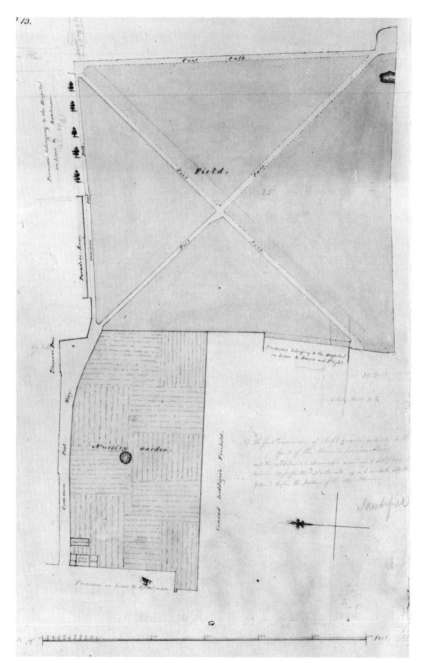

two sons helped him develop the Nursery into the family business, 'Conrad Loddiges and Sons'. Although settled with his family in London Joachim Conrad appears not to have become a British citizen. In 1805 he still required a permit from the Alien Office in Westminster.[56] Whether his relatives in Germany assisted in the development of the Nursery is not known, and neither is it clear whether John Busch was involved following his return from Russia in 1789.

The Head Gardener during the first part of the Nursery's occupation of land at Paradise Field, is believed to have been John Renton I (1747–1810). Renton had been the owner of the Hoxton Field Nursery and his son later painted and exhibited portraits of the Loddiges family.[57]

Redevelopment of Barbers Barn for Loddiges Place

One of the achievements during the first thirty-year period was to diversify into property development along the freehold frontage of the Nursery. Joachim Conrad Loddiges' freehold consisted of a six-hundred-foot long garden

Loddiges' Paradise Field Nursery
Early leasehold plan for St Thomas' Hospital c.1786
showing the principal leasehold fields which became the
Hackney Botanic Garden of C. Loddiges and Sons. The larger
field is the 'Seven Acre Field', the smaller 'Church Street
Field'. The common footway became Paragon Road.
Loddiges' freehold Barbers Barn land adjoins Church Street
Field to the south. Courtesy of the Greater London Record
Office

stretching back from a one-hundred-foot frontage on Mare Street.

Along the frontage was an old Elizabethan house, Barbers Barn, which was popular with late eighteenth-century engravers of local scenes. During part of the seventeenth century it had been the residence of Colonel John Okey of Cromwell's Army, one of the first of fifty-nine signatories to Charles I's death warrant. In the sixteenth century Lord Darnley, the second husband of Mary, Queen of Scots, had once stayed here.

Despite its importance, at the time of its purchase by Joachim Conrad Loddiges, Barbers Barn was in poor condition. Next to the old house, Joachim Conrad opened up a nursery entrance and built himself a modest home now replaced by the Royal London Assurance building, 222 Mare Street. Barbers Barn was later demolished and on its site Joachim Conrad built Loddiges Place, a row of four houses.[58] The new terrace stood on Mare Street between today's Darnley and Devonshire Road.[59]

Barbers Barn c.1750

Conrad Loddiges' contributions to *The Botanical Magazine*

The eighteenth and nineteenth centuries were a period of 'plant-hunting'. Voyages and expeditions led to new discoveries in the New World, China, and Australia. New species of plants were reported, described and illustrated in the first regular periodical to be devoted to their description, *The Botanical Magazine*. Founded in 1787 in London by the Quaker horticulturist and botanist William Curtis, it has remained in continuous publication to this day, and is presently published by the Royal Botanic Gardens, Kew. In the early 1800s, the periodical passed into the editorship of the Quaker horticulturist John

Family portraits by John Renton, son of the head gardener at Loddiges Nursery. Exhibited at the British Institute and the Royal Academy in 1821.

Joachim Conrad Loddiges

Jane Loddiges née Creighton

George Loddiges

Sims, who lost no time in praising Loddiges Nursery. Joachim Conrad Loddiges was described in *The Botanical Magazine* as 'this excellent cultivator', responsible for introducing 'many rare exotics into our gardens' and for 'the preservation and propagation of more, that would have been otherwise lost'.[60]

Sims had reason to be grateful, since two hundred of the fine coloured plates which appeared in the early editions of *The Botanical Magazine* had been drawn from exotic plants at Loddiges Nursery. When, in 1807, Joachim Conrad Loddiges produced a newly-discovered flower for illustration in *The Botanical Magazine*, John Sims responded by praising Loddiges' 'liberality in communicating his possessions for the promotion of science', for which 'the numbers of our magazine bear ample testimony'. Sims noted that the flower had not yet been given a botanical name and considered it 'a duty imposed upon us, thus to record his merits, by naming a genus after him.'[61]

The Oxalis-leaved Loddigesia *Loddigesia oxalidifolia* was illustrated as plate 965 in *The Botanical Magazine*.[62] It is a hardy, evergreen greenhouse shrub, which grows up to about two feet tall, with pale purple and white flowers. Sims, recalling how Carl Linnaeus, the originator of the modern system of plant classification, had sometimes amused himself 'fancying a resemblance between the genus and the person in whose honour it is dedicated', wrote light-heartedly comparing the plant with the nurseryman:

Oxalis-leaved Loddigesia. Courtesy of the British Museum

so in *Loddigesia* the minute white standard may be considered as the emblem of the modest pretensions of this venerable cultivator; the broad keels, of his real usefulness to science; and the far extended wings, as that of his two sons.[63]

Loddiges' plant-export business

Alongside the Nursery's increasing reputation as a specialist in the import and cultivation of rare exotic plants into Britain, it also developed a leading export role. Specialist packaging was needed to promote survival during long sea voyages, and few nurseries could compete:

> Loddiges in particular sent numbers of plants abroad, the firm being famous for its skill in packing. Their object was to retard the natural growth of plants during a long voyage till they reached the climate for which they were intended. To this effect Loddiges packed in layers with Sphagnum, a bad conductor, which was trodden or pressed down firmly.[64]

Between 1793 and 1815 the plant export trade was hampered by the war with France which ended with the Battle of Waterloo. A few years later the successful tea plantation on the island of Madeira was founded, partly from plants supplied by Loddiges Nursery.

🌿 The Hackney Botanic Nursery Garden (1816-49)

After 1816, Loddiges Nursery began to secure a unique position in the history of the trade. Popularised as 'The Hackney Botanic Nursery Garden' by the foremost horticultural journalist of the day, it embarked upon a series of prestigious developments.[65] These were to result in spectacular hothouses, a 'tropical rain forest' display and an arboretum which attracted visitors from all over Europe. Many of these developments bore the hallmark of Joachim Conrad Loddiges'

youngest son, George. It was he who established firm links with the scientific societies of the period and promoted the nursery through its publication, *The Botanical Cabinet*.[66]

Early in this period (1821), Joachim Conrad transferred the St Thomas' Hospital leases to his

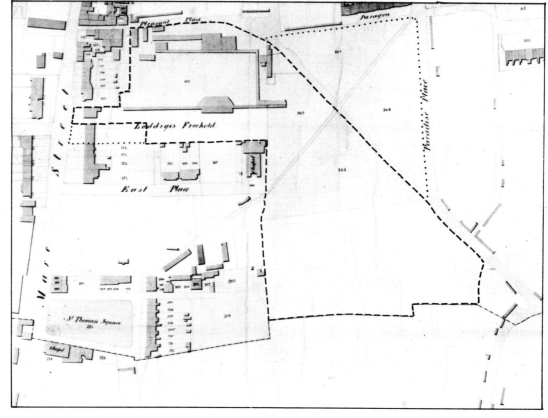

Loddiges Hackney Botanic Nursery Garden.
St Thomas' Hospital estate map showing numbered leasehold fields and properties (c.1830–50). William and George Loddiges' houses are shown (Mare Street freehold entrance and STH162 respectively). The large arboretum field is the freehold south of STH163. Courtesy of the Greater London Record Office

two sons, who took the option to extend their expiry from 1832 to 1853.[67] Unfortunately Joachim Conrad Loddiges was not able to see out this period. He was to die in 1826 at the age of 87.

Loddiges Place

In the decade after 1818 there were two notable occupants of Loddiges Place – the marine engraver George Cooke and his son, Edward. They moved here to work on *The Botanical Cabinet* (1817–33). Gazing from their front windows they would have seen a 'picturesque' view, with 'a delightful vista of forest trees' fringing the path. Lime trees fronted Loddiges Place, and elms grew in the gardens opposite. Such trees were not always loved. According to Benjamin Clarke, a local resident wrote to the parish magazine asking:

> What beauty can there be in a road-side tree even in leaf, and when bare, as in winter, it is ugly, and either aspect does not compensate for the damage to the highways?

Such opinions apparently prevailed against the more enlightened views of the Loddiges family who unsuccessfully campaigned to save the trees opposite Loddiges Place.[68]

The Cookes lived at Loddiges Place for eleven years before moving to Barnes in South London. Whilst living at Loddiges Place, George's son Edward developed his lifelong enthusiasm for ferns and flowering plants, influenced at an impressionable age by the redoubtable George Loddiges. Edward, when only nine years old, was commissioned to engrave the Nursery's plants for John Loudon's *Encyclopaedia of Plants*. Edward married Joachim Conrad's grand-daughter Jane in 1840. His horticultural work survives at the gardens at Biddulph Grange in Staffordshire, recently restored and opened to the public by the National Trust.

The experimental glasshouses and hothouses

If one experimental development gave the Hackney Botanic Nursery Garden particular fame and most astounded its visitors, it was its magnificent range of tropical hothouses.

In the nineteenth century it was common to make a distinction between the 'stove house' and the 'greenhouse'. Both were glazed, but the former required continuous heating whereas the latter required heat only to prevent frost damage. During the 1820s, except at nurseries such as Loddiges, potted plants in stove houses were often placed amongst waste oak bark from tanneries. The decomposing waste produced enough heat to warm the plants. After the 1830s a central heating system using steam was more widely used.[69]

Until the beginning of the nineteenth century, there had been few attempts at obtaining a moist heat without smell or smoky fumes. Poor standards in the manufacture of iron pipes had hampered the steam-heating technology used in experimental hothouses.[70] As cast iron technology developed, improved quality pipes could be fitted to airtight stoves. This modification allowed a single furnace to heat the nursery owner's residence as well as the greenhouses. Hence, by 1816, steam technology began to offer an effective heating system for nurseries that had struggled to raise tropical rain forest or hot desert plants in stove houses. The new small-bore cast-iron tubes could be sunk below latticed cast-iron paths, both manufactured by the firm of W. & D. Bailey & Co. of Holborn.[71]

Loddiges Nursery was quick to exploit the new technology. The earliest steam-heated stove house was probably constructed in 1816 or thereabouts. The Mauritius Fan Palm *Latania borbonica*, acquired in 1814, which became the prize of their collection, required stove conditions. In the early stove houses George Loddiges developed a rain sprinkler system consisting of pipes perforated by a needle along their length, and running horizontally below the roof of the stove houses. For this invention the Horticultural Society, now the Royal Horticultural Society, voted George Loddiges a medal in 1817. Three years later the Horticultural Society published a description of Loddiges' humidification system.[72]

By 1821 George Loddiges had built a house for himself. 'Loddiges House' stood in Paradise Field adjacent to the stove houses, conveniently sited for connection to the central-heating system of the Palm House and the associated hothouses.[73] His home and the eleven hundred feet of heated stove houses and greenhouses all derived their heat from one boiler.[74] Such a model scheme won praise from the Horticultural Society:

> The extraordinary health, and the flourishing conditions of the plants cultivated in these

houses are proofs of the superior advantages of this mode of heating.[75]

In the same year, plans were drawn up for the Palm House to be enlarged:

> It is understood that Messrs Loddiges have in contemplation the erection of a house of larger dimensions than any that has yet been formed, for the growth of palms.[76]

The completion of this ambitious scheme gave Loddiges the most famous tropical palm house in the world, pre-dating Kew's palm house by some twenty-four years. It needed no new boiler, taking steam from the single powerful boiler already in use.[77]

Loddiges Grand Palm House: the largest in the world

Loddiges' vast stove house at the Hackney Botanic Nursery Garden became known as the Grand Palm House. Here palms grew together as nowhere else in the world, set amidst an abundance of epiphytic orchids and other tropical plants. The sheer size of the building was impressive: John Loudon described it as 'the

Loddiges Palm House from the Pictorial Times

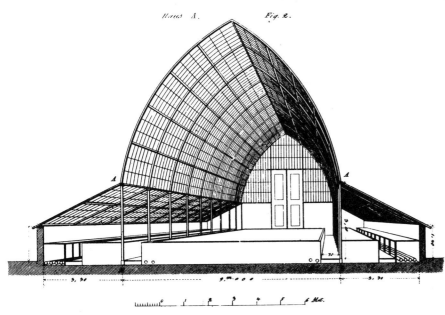

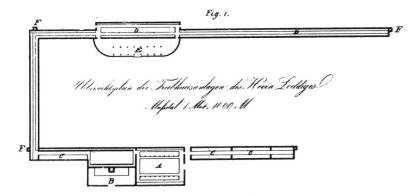

largest hot-house in the world', and this had certainly been Loddiges' intention. In 1825, Dr Schultes, a Bohemian professor and president of his university's botanic garden, recorded its measurements as 80ft long, 60ft wide and 40ft high.[78]

It was built in the form of a glass paraboloid, kept together by a delicate but strong frame of small iron ribs. Inside, the air was warmed by steam and there was a stage from which to view the tropical plants. Describing his visit to this tropical palm house in 1825, Dr Schultes wrote:

> In ascending to the upper part of it by an elegant stage thirty feet high, we thence enjoy a scene entirely novel to a native of Europe: the tropical plants of both hemispheres, the eastern and the western, are stretched out below at our feet.[79]

By 1826 the palm collection was so magnificent that in the very first volume of John Loudon's *The Gardener's Magazine*, three pages were devoted to listing all 120 species in cultivation at Loddiges Nursery. The publication detailed palms from over thirty countries and states including St Vincent, Brazil, Madagascar, Jamaica, Trinidad, Mauritius, Ceylon, Egypt, Gambia, South Africa.[80]

Visitors were impressed by the size of the palms and by the number of species on display. The palms flourished in the simulated tropical conditions and their growth required the constant enlargement of their planting boxes. In an article which John Loudon wrote about

Drawing of the Grand Palm House at Loddiges Nursery. Courtesy of the RIBA

London's nurseries, he reported one such operation, observed during a visit in April 1830:

> Some of the larger palms have had their boxes renewed and increased in size; the material, as before, the teak wood of old East India ships, which Messrs Loddiges find more durable than oak. The collection is constantly increasing by donations and purchases.[81]

The collection attracted numerous European visitors. In 1829 Jacob Rinz, a nurseryman from Frankfurt-am-Main, found his visit a magical and transporting experience:

> Never shall I forget the sensation produced by this establishment. I cannot describe the raptures I experienced on seeing that immense palm house. All that I had before seen of the kind appeared nothing to me compared with this. I fancied myself in the Brazils; and especially at that moment when Mr Loddiges had the kindness to produce, in my presence, a shower of artificial rain.[82]

Growing in these splendid tropical conditions were insectivorous plants (pitcher plants and sarracenias).[83] Orchid and fern collections were also being developed, and these too attracted special interest. The following description dates from 1833:

> In the palm house everything is in its usual luxuriance; the ferns are in most vigorous growth and the epiphytes flowering beautifully. *Oncidium divaricatum* and *flexuosum* and *Calathe veratrifolia* are extremely conspicuous. There is a beautiful new Lycopidium (*L. circinatum*), the thick-set branches of which can only compare to fine chenille work in embroidery. A shower of rain was let off to show the effect to a stranger who accompanied us. We mention this to remind our readers of what has been done in this way and what may be done again in lofty conservatories. The epiphytes which required props were elegantly supported by small twigs of bamboo, which are inconspicuous, found to be durable, and therefore very appropriate. The names of many of the plants were repainted with very thick black oil paint on Wright's porcelain tallies.[84]

Enquiring as to the catalogue value of all the palms Schultes had been told they were worth £200,000 in 1829. Still more palms were added. In the following year, *The Gardener's Magazine* noted that 'the collection is constantly increasing by donations and purchases from all quarters'.

By the early 1830s the Grand Palm House was overflowing with ferns, orchids and, of course palms. Expansion was required. A new palm house was designed by Joseph Paxton. It was the first example on any notable scale of the use of wood in a curved roof.[85] Paxton's laminated wood construction at Loddiges Nursery pre-dated his use of the same technique for a hothouse he built in 1836 at Chatsworth in which the first Victoria Regia lily flowered in Britain in 1849. Both constructions were forerunners of Paxton's first Crystal Palace, built at Hyde Park to house the 1851 Great Exhibition.

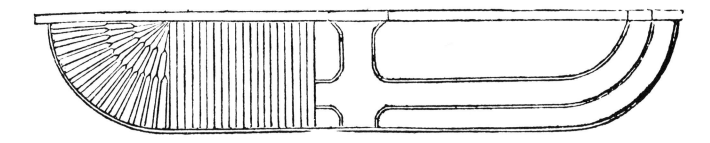

Loddiges Camellia House drawn for The Encyclopaedia of Gardening, *1822*

Loddiges Camellia House

Loddiges Camellia House employed John Loudon's invention of iron-framed curvilinear glazing on a massive scale and was one of the earliest glasshouses to employ it to produce a most attractive effect. The Camellia House was built from John Loudon's plans, and in its day it was almost as famous as the Grand Palm House. Both were steam-heated by the same central heating system.

The Camellia House was also noted for its scale: it was 120ft long, 23ft wide and 18ft high; it was roofed with copper sashes by the firm of Trimmins of Birmingham.[86] This huge structure was built in 1819–22 by Bailey & Co., the company to whom Loudon transferred his rights in 1818.[87] The Camellia House was one of the first of Bailey's commissions and it helped to make curvilinear glasshouses fashionable. Most were smaller than Loddiges Camellia House, taking the simple form of a half-dome abutting a wall. One surviving example, contemporary with Loddiges Camellia House, is at Bicton in Devon, where the palm house consists of three such half-domes built as an integral whole.[88]

The display of Loddiges' tropical and East Asian camellias undoubtedly benefitted from their special glasshouse, and in 1824, Bailey & Co. added a second Camellia House on the opposite side of the wall.[89] Inside the double Camellia

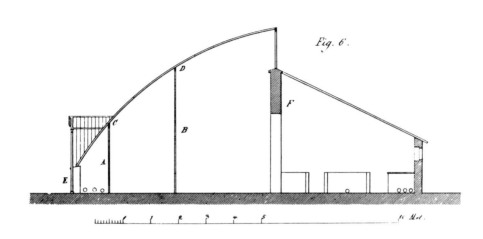

House there were a variety of other flowering shrubs and climbers to impress the visitor:

> In the Camellia House a *Wisteria consequana* runs along the roof in two horizontal lines, and has now its second crop of flowers. We are glad to find Mr George Loddiges of the opinion that this plant would soon be on every cottage front in the kingdom.[90]

The growing conditions were also perfected. Indeed their cultivation was so successful that the camellias may have virtually taken over their houses. In 1833 it was noted that 'the Camellia House … is a complete wood of that shrub, so much so that blackbirds have repeatedly built their nests and reared their young in it'.[91]

A tour of all the houses

By the early 1820s, eyewitness accounts suggest that Loddiges' tropical hothouses were a much-visited local attraction. This is how they appeared to the Quaker pharmacist William Allen, who lived on Church Street, Stoke Newington. He took his cousin Emily G. Birkbeck, and Anna Hanbury, to Loddiges Nursery on 30 March 1822, to see the splendid sights:

> We all went to Loddiges Nursery, to see the camellias which are now in full bloom and very beautiful! There is quite a forest of them: his hot-houses are, perhaps, the most capacious in the world: one of them is 40 feet high: in this there is a banana tree which nearly reaches the top.[92]

Section through Loddiges Camellia House. An early curvilinear glasshouse constructed by W. & D. Bailey to John Loudon's design

Even leaving aside the Grand Palm House and double Camellia House, the extent of steam-heated glasshouses was unusual at such an early date. They predated the repeal of the glass tax, the palm stove house at the Royal Botanic Garden in Edinburgh (1834), the magnificent stove conservatory at Chatsworth (1836-40), and Decimus Burton's famous palm house at the Royal Botanic Gardens, Kew (1848). Throughout the 1820s and for some time thereafter, Loddiges' collection of stove houses remained unsurpassed in Europe, or indeed the world.

> Besides this house [the Grand Palm House], there are some twenty others, from one hundred and fifty to three hundred feet long, and greenhouses of various dimensions ... one of the houses built after the newest plan with convex windows is stocked with nearly 400 kinds of heath ... We will venture to say, that much as we have travelled and seen, we have met with no stoves, belonging to prince, king or emperor, which can compare with those of Messrs Loddiges, at Hackney for the magnificence, convenience, and elegance of their plan, and the value of their contents.[93]

Further descriptions of the vast range of exotic hothouse plants were given in the late 1820s, when the conditions were found to be ideal: 'Under such natural and perfect management, the palms, ferns, and most other plants, appeared just as might be expected'.[94] Such quality and quantity proved indispensable for the production of John Loudon's classic book, *The Encyclopaedia of Plants*, published in 1829. Many of its illustrations had been drawn by the young Edward Cooke at Loddiges Nursery. The preface reads:

American collection

Arboretum

Propagating pits

Soils and pots

Bridge

Dry-stove bulbs

Grand palm house

Stoves

MARE STREET

Footpath (public lane)

Double camellia house

Greenhouse plants

Entrance

Loddiges' Paradise Field Nursery as mapped for
The Encyclopaedia of Gardening, *1834 edition*

[the Proprietors] beg leave to thank, in a very particular manner, Messrs Loddiges of Hackney for original drawings of many species made from living plants in their unrivalled collection of exotics. Without … the hot-houses of Messrs. Loddiges, this work could not have been produced.[95]

In 1834, John Loudon also published a detailed plan showing the layout of all the glasshouses and the outdoor arboretum. Through its main entrance in Mare Street the visitor passed at once to a range of hothouses leading to the quite remarkable Grand Palm House, then past the Dry Stove House to the two Camellia Houses and numerous greenhouses.[96] The buildings were arranged as a square, with herbaceous beds in the centre and potted plants for the visitor to buy.

The Grand Palm House and its orchids

By the 1820s, Loddiges Nursery was renowned for its tropical orchids. It is said to have been the first British firm to have cultivated them commercially.[97] Certainly Loddiges had an abundance of orchids in the early 1800s and for many years it was the principal supplier of the plants. Their infatuation with epiphytic tropical orchids is said to have arisen in 1812 after the nursery had received a plant of *Oncidium bifolium*:

from a gentleman who bought it from Monte Video, and who informed them that it was hung up in the cabin without earth, and continued to flower during a great part of the voyage home; a statement which was then regarded as

a traveller's tale and beyond the limits of credulity.

The Loddiges were amongst the earliest to realise that, since epiphytes grow without soil, this was fact rather than fiction, and quickly opened up a trade in imported epiphytic orchids.[98]

Many of the orchids available from Loddiges

Mr Loddiges' Acropera **Acropera loddigesii**. *A splendid orchid named in honour of Joachim Conrad Loddiges. Illustration from* The Botanical Magazine, *1837. By permission of the British Library*

Nursery in the 1820s and 30s were illustrated in *The Botanical Cabinet*, which also named the correspondents who first collected them. By 1825 the nursery had 84 species for sale.

However, orchids were most unsuitable as household ornaments: they were difficult to culti-vate and it was especially difficult to make them flower. Sir Joseph Banks noted dryly that during the first two decades of the nineteenth century England became 'the grave of tropical orchids'. Few nurseries apart from Loddiges had the expertise to raise them successfully. Some private collectors, upon receiving their precious tropical orchids from other suppliers, immediately packed them off to Loddiges Nursery to be encouraged to flower.

After his father's death in the 1820s, George Loddiges developed the tropical orchid collection further, growing many species new to science in the perfect conditions of the Grand Palm House. In appreciation of this work, Dr Lindley named an unusual epiphytic Mexican orchid Loddiges Acropera *Acropera loddigesii*.[99] In 1837, *The Botanical Magazine* described and illustrated the orchid as:

> a very singular epiphytous orchideous plant, introduced into the stoves of this country from Xalapa of Mexico by Mr George Loddiges … The habit of the plant is quite peculiar; the racemes [flower spikes] are quite pendent.

A second orchid was also named after George Loddiges: *Cattleya loddigesii* from Brazil, which is now sold as a house plant in various cultivar forms.[100] Throughout the 1830s George continued his specialist interest in cultivating and displaying epiphytic orchids. His novel techniques, as described by this eyewitness, attracted considerable acclaim:

> The first hot-house we entered is chiefly devoted to orchidaceous epiphytes; a number

of which are tied on pieces of the stems or branches of trees with their bark on (about two or three inches in diameter and six or eight inches long), and suspended from the roof by wires. A small tuft of moss is first put on the upper side of the piece of wood; on this the plant is placed, a little green moss is then put over the roots and the whole is visible from below. The plants in this situation thrive most vigorously, sending their roots from under the moss down each side, closely embracing the piece of wood, and each plant seeming as though it were riding astride on its little barrel-like wooden horse. This mode of growing epiphytes is at once, very successful and very curious.[101]

By 1839 George Loddiges had increased the Nursery's range of tropical orchids and was well placed to publish the firm's first catalogue devoted entirely to these plants. Over 1,600 species were listed for general sale. A decade later the collection of tropical plants, including orchids, was still unrivalled.

> The collection of orchids, palms and ferns assembled in the stoves at Hackney by Mr Loddiges' untiring zeal and munificent expenditure are unrivalled in extent, – the orchids alone amounting in the year 1845, to 1,916 species and varieties, and the palms to 280.[102]

The popularity of the tropical orchid spread from being a specialist interest amongst cultivators to a domestic Victorian fashion. This was perhaps inevitable, given the exotic appearance of the flowers and their association with hitherto unexplored corners of the globe. Some also commanded attention on account of their enormous size.[103] Enthusiasts such as James Bateman, whose orchid book had larger plates than any other botanical book, advised his well-to-do readers that orchids were 'an indispensable adjunct to a place of any consideration'.[104] Long after Loddiges Nursery closed down, the orchid craze continued unabated.

The Grand Palm House and 'The Victorian Fern Craze'

Besides encouraging rare orchids to flower, the Grand Palm House also aided the Nursery's propagation of exotic ferns. As with tropical orchids, Loddiges' pioneering attempts at cultivation of both exotic and temperate ferns helped to create a late Victorian fashion. Due to its experiments and influence, fern growing, fern books, and fern cases became commonplace in middle class households. David Allen, in *The Victorian Fern Craze* accords Loddiges Nursery a pivotal role:

> Fern raising might have been for far longer a recondite art, confined to curators, had the great firm of Hackney nurserymen Conrad Loddiges and Sons not now been tempted to take up the torch.

In 1866, when John Smith, the fern specialist from the Royal Botanic Gardens at Kew, published *Ferns: British and Foreign*, he gave the credit for the spread of fern cultivation to Loddiges Nursery.

The role of Loddiges Nursery can be overstated. Properly, some of the credit should have

*I*n 1830 Nathaniel Ward discovered that seeds would grow into healthy plants when kept in an almost air-tight glass bottle. Inside the bottle, plants were virtually self-supporting, needing only a little damp soil or moss; their respiration took up oxygen roughly in balance with the production of this gas through photo-synthesis. This process of gaseous exchange by plants was not yet understood by scientists, but the begin-

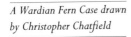

Rectangular fern case

nings of an understanding had arisen from the research of Dr Joseph Priestley. Priestley, who lived nearby in Clapton Passage, Hackney, before emigrating to America in 1795, had discovered that air was composed of several gases and that plants improved its life-giving qualities.[106] Despite the absence of a more complete scientific explanation, Ward was fascinated by his own discovery. He communicated it to George Loddiges, who quickly realised its commercial potential. In future, the most delicate of plants could be bought for display and flourish under household conditions despite the polluted city air. There was also the possibility of safer sea transport for plants.

A Wardian Fern Case drawn by Christopher Chatfield

Economic botany: packaging and transporting plants for Kew

Salty sea-air is harmful to many plants, and before the 1830s the transport-ing of plants by sea was unsatisfactory. In November 1834 news came that the young plants sent by George Loddiges inside protect-ive Wardian Cases, had arrived safely in Australia after a four-month voyage.

Rosher's fern pillar

John Loudon enthused that: 'the success attend-ing to [these] experiments opens up extensive views as to other applications in transporting plants from one place to another'. The cases were refilled with other plants for the return journey. When they arrived in Britain, Ward and George Loddiges went to inspect them. They were overjoyed. Ward wrote: 'I will not readily forget the delight expressed by Mr George Loddiges, who accompanied me on board, at the beautiful appearance of **Gleichenia micro-phylla**, a plant now seen for the first time alive in this country'.

One of the first to use the new technique was the Duke of Devonshire. On the advice of John Lindley, Professor of Botany at University College London, the Duke sent John Gibson, his assistant gardener, to Loddiges Nursery, preparatory to a trip to India in 1835 to collect plants for Chatsworth. In 1836 William Hooker's Companion to The Botanical Magazine published full details of the new method of conveying plants.[107]

Thereafter the Royal Botanic Gardens, Kew used the Wardian Case technique in their economic botany work. Tiny saplings of banana trees were transported to Asia and Africa using sealed cases, and quinine-producing plants were transported to India to help treat malaria. The cases were so successfully employed that the directors of Kew Gardens began to plan even more large scale movements of plants and they eventually succeeded in establishing tea as a cash crop in India (from China) and rubber in Malaya (from South America). The Royal Botanic Gardens, Kew continued using Wardian Cases up to the 1940s.[108] Today air-tight polythene bags have replaced glass plant cases to keep plants and cut flowers fresh.

Wardian Case

The 'Victorian Fern Craze'

As George Loddiges realised, the new cases enabled his clients to grow ferns and orchids at home more successfully than hitherto. By 1833 Ward and Loddiges had succeeded in growing thirty species of fern in miniature 'greenhouses' made airtight with putty and clay. They had also succeeded in growing the difficult saprophytic Bird's-nest Orchid **Neottianidus avis**; Ward published nothing of his experimental work with George Loddiges until December of this year.[109]

Nathaniel Ward described his plant cases to a wider audience in John Loudon's Gardener's Magazine in 1839, and thereafter in his book On the Growth of Plants in Closely Glazed Cases. The book was illustrated by George Loddiges' son-in-law Edward Cooke and completed for publication in 1842. In 1845 John Lindley and Ward lobbied for the repeal of the glass tax. The repeal of this tax made the cases affordable. This, combined with the public interest aroused by their exhibition at The Great Exhibition in Hyde Park in 1851 (complete with luxuriant ferns provided by Conrad Loddiges), transformed fern cases into fashionable household items. As the air pollution in London and the big cities worsened, so the appeal of fern cases increased.[110] However they were never widely used for the more philanthropic purposes Ward had in mind: to enable fresh salad foods to be grown by the poor in smoky cities.

gone to the Liverpool Botanic Garden and to Captain Bligh of *Mutiny on the Bounty* fame. It was Bligh who in 1795 brought thirty seven species of fern to Britain from the West Indies. Credit was also due to Robert Morison, the Oxford professor who first grew ferns from spores and observed their unusual 'alternation of generations' life-cycle in 1699.

In 1825, the ferns in Loddiges Grand Palm House rivalled the royal collection being established at the gardens of Kew Palace. The number of exotic species exceeded one hundred. Not all were for sale. In 1828 a purchaser could choose from amongst eighty different types of exotic fern, covering nearly forty genera. At this date Loddiges had a 'near monopoly of the fern trade … derived in part from the great reputation and experience acquired over many years.'[105]

George William Francis FLS (1800–65), a scientific friend of George Loddiges and fellow microscopist who served a 'gentlemen's apprenticeship' at Loddiges Nursery under George Loddiges, and went on to become the first Director of the Adelaide Botanic Garden, published the first book on British ferns for fifty years in 1837. This book, together with the work of nurseries such as Loddiges, and the invention of the Wardian Fern Case, led to the 'Victorian Fern Craze'.

The Hackney Botanic Nursery Arboretum

Besides the outstanding hothouses, and the burgeoning fern and orchid business, the Hackney Nursery attracted many visitors to its outdoor grounds. John Harvey, the horticultural historian, noted that 'Loddiges also planted an arboretum, begun in 1816, one of the first in Britain.'[111] A decade later the arboretum was even more extensive. In Loddiges' catalogue there were 2,664 hardy trees and shrubs, including roses and climbers, most of them displayed in the arboretum.

To find these, the visitor would take a path from the hothouse or begin directly from the Mare Street entrance. Upon crossing over a footbridge which spanned a public lane, the visitor entered the start of the arboretum, a carefully laid-out spiral walk with specimen trees arranged alphabetically along the right-hand side of the path. In 1833, *The Gardener's Magazine* commented on the novelty of the walk:

> The arboretum looks better this season than it has ever done since it was planted … The more lofty trees suffered from the late high winds, but not materially. We walked round the two outer spirals of this coil of trees and shrubs; viz. from *Acer* to *Quercus*. There is no garden scene about London so interesting.[112]

On the left-hand side of each spiral path lay Loddiges Rosarium – a collection of nearly a thousand different species and varieties. In 1893,

RIGHT *True Service Tree*
Sorbus domestica
drawn at Loddiges Nursery
for John Loudon's
Arboretum et
Fruticetum Britannicum,
1838. For many years the
Nursery was the principal
supplier of this rare tree.
BELOW *Queen Mary's*
Hawthorn **Crataegus**
oxyacantha *'Regina'*
which the nursery propa-
gated from a famous tree
associated with Mary,
Queen of Scots.

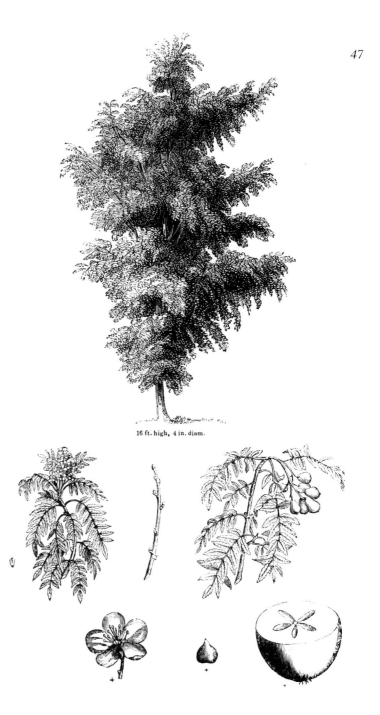

16 ft. high, 4 in. diam.

14 ft. high, 2½ in. diam.

a neighbour, Dr Benjamin Clarke recalled visiting this beautiful rose garden:

> The rose plot was a gem and was somewhere about where Loddiges Road now runs. It was a circular plot with circles of the finest and most velvety grass cut up into smaller plots, forming segments of the circles, each filled with every variety of rose then known, and roses did bloom in Hackney sixty years ago![113]

The rosarium was followed, in the spirals of the arboretum walk, by assorted herbaceous plants. At the end of the walk lay a special American collection of select shrubs and flowers.

The arboretum was planned with commercial principles in mind. Although the stock at the front of each row was not for sale, being left to grow into natural shapes and sizes, the rows behind exhibited younger stock of the same trees, shrubs, and roses, all available for public sale. Loddiges' 1830 catalogue listed a colossal 3,075 hardy trees and shrubs grown in these beds.

In 1834 the botanic garden was said to have contained 'all the trees and shrubs which will grow in the open air, with the exception of some of the more common species'.[114] As such it was not only one of the earliest, but actually the largest collection of trees in Britain. Even with popular specialist groups such as pines, Loddiges held the most complete collection of any nursery in Britain. Its hawthorn collection was the subject of special comment:

> It is surprising that this genus is so little culti-vated in shrubberys. Messrs Loddiges have upwards of sixty species and varieties in their

arboretum [in 1828], all of which are beautiful, and so obviously of the thorn kind, that the most superficial observer would never mistake them for any other tree. An acre laid out as a thornery would form an interesting episode to the general scenery of a pleasure-ground.[115]

The Nursery's interest in new species of hawthorn was honoured by the French botanist René Desfontaines, who named the Mexican Hawthorn *Crataegus loddigesiana*, out of respect for George Loddiges.[116] Amongst ordinary visitors, even the colours of the trees sparked amazement:

> The Acers, which furnish the yellows in the American forests, are in great luxuriance at Messrs Loddiges. The birches, which furnish the reds, yellows and browns, are also very fine. What a treasure …[117]

Apart from its sheer scale, its novelty, and the rarity of some of its trees and shrubs, even the labelling was unique. This was taken far more seriously than elsewhere, even to the point of varnishing over all the labels in order to preserve them – a practice not even carried out at the Horticultural Society's Chiswick Garden at so early a date.[118]

As with its vast orchid collection and palm col-lection, Loddiges' Arboretum was quite simply unsurpassed:

> There is no such collection of hardy trees and shrubs in the world; and when it is considered that they may all enter our plantations, their value to the country is incalculable. In this department, Messrs Loddiges have done more

than all the royal and botanic gardens put together.[119]

Today the only images which survive are the engravings in John Loudon's encyclopaedic tome on the trees and shrubs of Britain, *Arboretum et Fruticetum Britannicum*. The eight volumes, published in 1838, include over 2,500 small drawings and 364 full page plates, many of which were made at the Loddiges Hackney Botanic Nursery Arboretum.[120]

13 ft. high, 6 in. diam.

Strawberry Tree **Arbutus andrachne**
drawn at Loddiges Nursery c.1838

The Hackney Botanic Nursery Garden: a conclusion

So luxuriant and diverse was the Hackney Botanic Nursery Garden, so magnificent and unusual its glasshouses, and so complete its collection of trees and shrubs, that it is hard today to believe that one nursery could have achieved all this. At the time, recognition came from many quarters, including the Horticultural Society, now the Royal Horticultural Society, which awarded *Messrs Loddiges* numerous medals throughout this period. The earliest known medals date from 1818 and 1819, and all are listed below:

1818	Horticultural Society	Silver Medal
1819	Horticultural Society	Silver Medal
1823	Horticultural Society	Sir Joseph Banks Memorial Portrait Prize Silver Medal
1826	Horticultural Society	Sir Joseph Banks Memorial Portrait Prize Silver Medal
1832	Horticultural Society	Sir Joseph Banks Memorial Portrait Prize Silver Medal
1835	Horticultural Society	Sir Joseph Banks Memorial Portrait Prize Gold Medal
1835	Horticultural Society	Sir Joseph Banks Memorial Portrait Prize Gold Medal
1835	Metropolitan Society of Florists and Amateurs	Gold Medal
1836	Horticultural Society	President's Silver Medal
1837	Horticultural Society	Silver Flora Medal
1851	Great Exhibition	Bronze Exhibitor's Medal

CHAPTER FOUR
🌿*The Botanical Cabinet (1817-33)*

Throughout the Nursery's history, the Loddiges family introduced many foreign plants into Britain, and thereby into our parks and gardens. The correspondents, and the many rare plants they supplied, would not be known to us were it not that George Loddiges illustrated his enormous plant collection in his own full-colour publication, *The Botanical Cabinet*.[121]

The publication was founded in 1817 with 270 subscribers, including Sir Joseph Banks, and the Dukes of Argyll, Bedford, Richmond, Atholl and Devonshire. With at least one edition each year, *The Botanical Cabinet* ran to twenty volumes during the Regency, and the reigns of George IV and William IV. In many ways it was an extension of the Loddiges' pioneering catalogues: a colour guide to the plants which could be seen, drawn, or bought at the Hackney Botanic Nursery Garden. On the title page of each volume George Cooke was credited for the magnificent engravings within. These were the main, and indeed almost the sole, feature of the publication.[122] The text has hitherto been noted only for its brevity and piety:

> The figures are often neat and pretty but the work has not the slightest claim to the title 'Botanical'. The letterpress is exceedingly meagre and largely impregnated with pious ejaculations and admonitions.[123]

The text is, however, of unique historical value in reconstructing Loddiges' vast network of correspondents and the dates of the Nursery's plant introductions.

The brevity of the text was probably intentional in order to avoid openly challenging the other full-colour botanical periodical of the period, *The Botanical Magazine*. Shortly before the first issue of *The Botanical Cabinet*, the Loddiges brothers wrote to John Sims, editor of *The Botanical Magazine* to 'beg acceptance of our new work which will appear in May'. Sims was assured that the new publication was 'not in any way intended as opposition to *The Botanical Magazine*'.[124] Nonetheless, there was some competition, as evidenced by John Loudon's *Encyclopaedia of Plants*, published in 1829. In referring the reader to the published description of the listed plants, *The Botanical Cabinet* was frequently given as the most appropriate source publication, although for a good number of other plants, *The Botanical Magazine* was quoted. Such competition was, however, both modest and short-lived, for *The Botanical Cabinet* had only a small number of wealthy subscribers and could not be reprinted since all 2,000 copper plates were stolen and replaced by cardboard.[125]

Title page and specimen
pages from The Botanical
Cabinet.
TOP RIGHT
Phyllanthus
turbinatus.
BELOW **Rondeletia**
speciosa.
Courtesy of the British
Museum

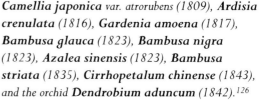

Catalogue

OF

PLANTS,

IN THE COLLECTION OF

CONRAD LODDIGES & SONS,

NURSERYMEN,

AT

HACKNEY,

NEAR

LONDON.

———

THE FOURTEENTH EDITION.

════════════

London:···Printed by
W. WILSON, 57, SKINNER-STREET.
1826.

Catalogue of plants.
Courtesy of the
British Museum.

*L*oddiges Nursery introduced into general cultivation in Britain a variety of plants from South Africa, Australia, the East Indies, China and the Americas.

Chinese plants

Amongst plants which made their début at Loddiges Nursery, were a number of Chinese plants. The following were introduced by Messrs Loddiges:

Camellia japonica var. atrorubens (1809), **Ardisia crenulata** (1816), **Gardenia amoena** (1817), **Bambusa glauca** (1823), **Bambusa nigra** (1823), **Azalea sinensis** (1823), **Bambusa striata** (1835), **Cirrhopetalum chinense** (1843), and the orchid **Dendrobium aduncum** (1842).[126]

One particular Chinese climber attracted particular attention – the elegant **Wisteria consequana** (syn. **W. sinensis**). Probably our most beautiful climber, it was discovered in the garden of Consequa. In May 1816 the first plant was shipped to Britain on behalf of a private owner in Surrey and was propagated at Loddiges Nursery.[127] Although later found to be hardy, it was first grown in the warmth of their Camellia House:

Wisteria.
Courtesy of the RHS

In the Camellia House a **Wisteria consequana** runs along the roof in two horizontal lines, and has now its second crop of flowers [June 21 1833]. We were glad to find Mr George Loddiges of the opinion that this plant (now sold by retail at from 1s 6d to 3s each, according to size) would soon be on every cottage front in the kingdom - a result which, our readers are aware, we have been desirous to bring about ever since this plant was introduced.[128]

Plants from Central Europe

From Central Europe, a popular garden flower which made its début at Loddiges Nursery was the tall, blue scabious **Scabiosa caucasia,** *introduced in 1803. The beautiful Siberian lily* **Lilium buschianum** *was introduced in 1829.*

American plants

Loddiges Nursery was noted for raising North American plants which had just been discovered, particularly trees and shrubs. The firm's most important supplier was the celebrated Quaker plant collector and traveller William Bartram (son of John Bartram). Seed was

also received from his rival André Michaux, who mainly collected for the French government.[129] When **Azalea calendulacea** was illustrated in The Botanical Cabinet, George Loddiges described it as: 'a native of Carolina and Virginia, on mountains, also of Georgia, where it was found in 1744 by our late venerable friend William Bartram, who in his travels gives this most glowing description of its beauty'. After William Bartram died his family stayed in contact with Loddiges Nursery. In 1823, shortly after William's death, the plant collector David Douglas visited Bartram's botanic garden in Philadelphia and Anne Carr gave him a small box of **Andromeda arborea** 'containing about twelve plants on condition that half should be given to Mr George Loddiges'.[130]

From Michaux, Conrad Loddiges received seed of **Andromeda catesbaei** in 1794. As with other early introductions of American plants, it was still being grown in 1828–30 when a fresh specimen was illustrated in The Botanical Cabinet. *Various species of mulberry, dogwood and rhododendron were also introduced into Britain at Loddiges Nursery from seed provided by Michaux.*[131]

CHAPTER FIVE

❧*Trees and plants for famous parks and gardens*

A firm commercial purpose lay behind the splendid exotic hothouses, rare trees, and flowers, at the Hackney Botanic Nursery Garden. Loddiges' palms and orchids would regularly fetch £5 each in the 1830s. Original records of sales still exist to several botanic gardens on mainland Europe, and for the Royal Botanic Gardens at Kew Palace. Similar records have not yet been traced for sales to large country estates such as Chatsworth and Woburn, but their archives may well contain records. Sales to these and other establishments are widely referred to in *The Botanical Cabinet* and *Arboretum et Fruticetum Britannicum*, as are sales to the Royal Parks and to Abney Park Cemetery, London's Nonconformist cemetery where some members of the Loddiges family are buried.

Plants supplied to botanic gardens

Plants for Kew

The records of sales by Loddiges' to Kew Palace, some as early as 1802, have survived in the Kew Archives.[132] One is signed by William Loddiges and dated 6 April 1806. It records a large number of purchases made by William Townsend Aiton, who was in charge of the royal collection at that date.[133] Amongst purchases made in 1802, one

entry was later annotated by Mr J. Smith, first curator of the Royal Botanic Gardens, Kew 1841–64. Smith's annotation, dated 1854, indicates that he had successfully identified one of the trees that had been bought from Loddiges Nursery some forty-eight years earlier, a specimen of the conifer *Thuia filiformis* subsequently named *Thuia occidentalis* 'Filiformis'.[134]

In spite of such sales, the royal garden had not been a regular customer of Loddiges Nursery. Supply from the Nursery is believed to have increased only when the Royal Botanic Gardens were established for public benefit from 1840–5 onwards.

The increase in business reflected the high regard in which the first Director of the Royal Botanic Gardens, Kew, William J. Hooker, held George Loddiges, who was amongst the first to send congratulations to Hooker on his appointment, expressing pleasure that Hooker, then in Scotland, would now be 'so near us'. Hooker, on his appointment, lost no time in inviting George Loddiges to supply plants to the new 'public' gardens. Within weeks, the necessary arrangements had been made and the curator Mr J. Smith visited the Nursery.

Hitherto, as George Loddiges confided to Hooker, 'we have been in the habit of dealing with most of the gardens of Europe, of which

Kew has been the exception'.[135] It is likely that the Nursery's relations with Kew had been impaired since 1824, when George Loddiges had been asked to give evidence in defence of an accused colleague at the Old Bailey.[136] At a trial before Mr Justice Best, a fellow nurseryman, Mr Robert Sweet of Colville's Nursery in west London, was charged with feloniously receiving seven plants in seven pots, knowing them to have been stolen from the gardens of Kew Palace. Owing to the value of the plants, this was a capital charge. George Loddiges suspected that Robert Sweet had been unfairly accused by William Townsend Aiton, Head Gardener at Kew Palace, with whom Sweet had recently had a dis-agreement. George Loddiges provided one of several character references, and the jury returned a verdict of not guilty.

Plants for European botanic gardens

The other botanic gardens with which George Loddiges traded, included the Geneva Botanic Garden. In 1833 Prof. A.D. Condolle of the botanic garden, exchanged plants with the Loddiges brothers. In 1837 the Juliusspital Botanic Garden, Würzburg, bought palms, orchids and other plants from Loddiges Nursery. What is noticeable from these and other pur-chases, is the high price paid to Loddiges Nursery for its exotic palms and orchids compared to the prices paid to other London nurseries for more temperate plants. In 1837, the Juliusspital Botanic Garden paid only £1 or less for most of its rare plants, but a quarter of those bought from

Loddiges Nursery cost £5 5s. These included a catechu nut palm, coconut palm, prickly sago palm and a fan palm.[140]

Adelaide Botanic Garden

Besides benefitting from Loddiges' trees and shrubs, botanic gardens also made use of Loddiges' experienced staff. Nowhere was the link as strong as with Adelaide in South Australia. On 31 May 1839 the Colonial Governor, Governor Gawley, appointed John Bailey, a botanist with twenty years experience at Loddiges Nursery, as Colonial Botanist. He was charged with setting up Adelaide's first botanic garden. A record in the Department of Lands reads, 'Botanical Garden, established in 1839. The site was selected by John Bailey and Governor Gawley, on 8 June 1839'. Two cottages, an office and a residence were built for John Bailey, and he was promised £80 per year towards the upkeep of the botanic garden, and the freedom to grow and sell his own nursery stock rent-free.

Nonetheless, the upkeep of the botanical garden proved uneconomic and in 1842 Bailey left to set up a commercial nursery to the east of Adelaide. He called it 'The Hackney Nursery'. Its location is today marked by two roads, Hackney Road and Nursery Road and this district of Adelaide is known as Hackney.

As for the public botanical garden, this was eventually managed by George Francis, a close friend of George Loddiges who had been a co-founder of the Microscopical Society and had learnt the art of nursery management at Loddiges

KEW GARDENS

The origin of the plant collection at Kew stems from the interest in plants shown by Princess Augusta, daughter-in-law of George II. She made a determined effort to establish a botanic garden in nine acres of the palace grounds in the decade before her death in 1772.

The Kew Palace collection did not achieve widespread recognition until it came into the hands of George III.

The King's plant collection was built-up with the help of Sir Joseph Banks. Banks, one of the founding members of the Horticultural Society, was well placed to raise the status of the garden. During his famous voyage with Captain Cook (1768–71) he discovered the botanical treasures of Australia, drying his herbarium on the beach thereafter called Botany Bay. Many of the plant discoveries made by Banks, Flinders, Masson and others were kept in specially prepared grounds or in the two specially prepared conservatories at Kew, purpose built by George III. The collection was managed initially by William Aiton (1731–93), and later by his son William Townsend Aiton (1766–1849), both of whom are buried in St Anne's Church, Kew Green.

In 1789 the royal collection contained 5,600 species of exotic plants, fewer than grew at Upton in the private garden of John Fothergill, an eminent Quaker horticulturist. By this date, even with royal patronage, it was difficult to keep up with the pace of newly imported plants. Whereas during the reign of George I a mere 182 plant species were imported

The development of Kew Gardens, 1760–1905

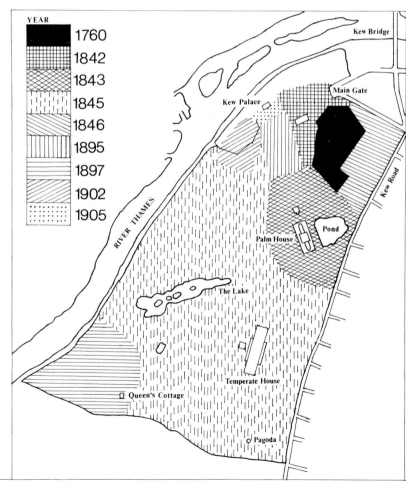

YEAR
1760
1842
1843
1845
1846
1895
1897
1902
1905

Kew Bridge

Main Gate

Kew Palace

Kew Road

Pond

Palm House

RIVER THAMES

The Lake

Temperate House

Queen's Cottage

Pagoda

into Britain, under George II the figure rose to 1,170, and under George III to 6,765.

In 1820, George III and Sir Joseph Banks died, and in the subsequent reigns of George IV and William IV, the gardens were simply neglected. Thus by 1829, visiting horticulturists from the continent found the 'largest collection of any' not at the royal palace, but at major commercial nurseries in London such as the nurseries of Lee and Loddiges.[137]

In the late 1830s, following William IV's death, a report on the future of the royal gardens at Kew was prepared by John Lindley, the first Professor of Botany at University College London. Lindley's report advocated opening the palace grounds as a public garden and their development into a centre for horticultural science. The Treasury explored other options, asking the Horticultural Society whether they would simply take away the most interesting plants, and re-erect the conservatories in their own grounds. Embarrassment followed from their refusal, and prompted the government to accept Lindley's report.

In March 1841, Kew's new role was secured by the appointment of Sir William Hooker as its first Director.[138] He had oversight of fifteen acres of the palace grounds, but these were gradually extended, such that by 1890 the full extent were open to the public. Kew's pre-eminence as a botanic garden important for its

science, re-emerged quickly after Hooker's appointment. In 1845 an arboretum was begun, and in 1848 the famous palm house, designed by Decimus Burton, was opened. Nonetheless, its collections remained surpassed by others. Charles Knight's 'London' (1851) noted that: 'the arboretum of Kew is now greatly inferior not only to the collections in the gardens of the Horticultural Society, but even to that of a private establishment, Messrs Loddiges' at Hackney.'[139] However, by this date the Nursery was preparing for closure, and its collection of exotics and trees would soon be eclipsed by the Royal Botanic Gardens.

The Palm House at Kew which opened in 1848, more than twenty years after the Grand Palm House at Loddiges Nursery in Hackney

PALM HOUSE, KEW.

Nursery. Francis became an influential figure in establishing an elected City Council for Adelaide, and became the first Director of the Adelaide Botanic Garden, which survives to this day.

Plants supplied to country estates

Plants supplied to Whiteknights

The acquisition and cultivation of newly introduced trees, shrubs and other plants stretched the resources of many enthusiasts, but none more spectacularly than the Marquis of Blandford, heir to the Duke of Marlborough. In 1798 he acquired Whiteknights, near Reading (now Reading University), and within twenty years only the Duke of Bedford's plant collection at Woburn is said to have paralleled his own.

Plants bought from Loddiges Nursery included newly discovered American trees and shrubs grown from seeds supplied by William Bartram. When the nursery received one hundred seeds of the pine *Pinus resinosa*, almost the whole of the resulting one hundred saplings were bought by the Marquis for Whiteknights.

Such was the cost that when the Marquis succeeded as Duke in 1817, he bore debts of over £1.5 million. In 1819 he sold his splendid Whiteknights to reside in a corner of the family's Bleinheim estate.

Plants supplied to Woburn Abbey

Amongst customers for Loddiges' plants was the Duke of Bedford, seeking plants for his world-renowned collection at Woburn Abbey.[141] Some flowered at Woburn before they flowered at Loddiges Nursery:

> We raised [*Erica obtusa*] in the year 1820, from Cape seeds: a plant of it we had sent to the Duke of Bedford, flowered for the first time last spring at Woburn. His Grace kindly communicated the specimen to us, and soon after some of our plants also produced flowers.[142]

Such cape heathers were a speciality of Loddiges Nursery. In the early nineteenth century, the exploration of the Cape for rare plants, was in its heyday.[143]

Plants supplied to Chatsworth House

Loddiges Nursery, besides supplying White Knights and Woburn with trees, shrubs, ferns and orchids, frequently sent plants to other country estates, notably to Chatsworth House in Derbyshire. Joseph Paxton was Chatsworth's head gardener and the owner, the Duke of Devonshire, was a frequent visitor by carriage to Loddiges Nursery.[144]

Plants supplied to royal parks

In 1831 John Loudon's *The Gardener's Magazine* ran an article urging that all new public parks, including London's royal parks, should copy the splendid arboretum walk laid out by Messrs Loddiges at their Hackney Nursery:

> The time is just commencing for the establishment of public parks and gardens adjoining towns, in which the beau ideal of this descrip-

Chatsworth House in the early nineteenth century, seat of the Duke of Devonshire, a prestigious figure in the Horticultural Society and regular client of Loddiges Nursery

tion of scenery [the foregoing description of Loddiges' arboretum] will be realised, at the expense of all, and for the enjoyment of all. The whole of Regent's Park would be required to plant one of each of the species and varieties contained in Messrs Loddiges' arboretum, at proper distances, varied by suitable glades; Hyde Park and Kensington Gardens would form another scene for a similar plantation; and a third might be formed of Greenwich Park.[145]

Plants for St James' Park and Kensington Gardens

Loddiges Nursery certainly supplied trees and shrubs for St James' Park and Kensington Gardens. The Commissioner for Woods and Forests ordered the rarities to be labelled, a task that required the identification talents of George Don. Don's labelling was so clear and comprehensive that a few years later, writing in *The Gardener's Magazine*, John Loudon was able to recommend use of the St James' Park and Kensington Gardens as a reference collection:

having correctly named the trees and shrubs supplied by Messrs Loddiges to St James' Park and Kensington Gardens, any country nurseryman may bring in or send in specimens, and correct their names by these living plants.[146]

Plants supplied to the new garden cemeteries

Six garden cemeteries were laid out in Britain between 1821 and 1832, the first being The Rosary in Norwich. This was followed by Catholic and Protestant cemeteries in Liverpool, Dublin and Glasgow. In 1830 George Carden, a barrister who had promoted burial reform throughout the previous decade, set up the first cemetery company in London. Its cemetery at Kensal Green became the first to open in London. Thereafter, six more London cemeteries were laid out within just eight years:

1833	Kensal Green	23ha (56acres)
1837	Norwood	16ha (39acres)
1839	Highgate	15ha (37acres)
1840	Brompton	16ha (39acres)
1840	Abney Park	13ha (32acres)
1840	Nunhead	21ha (52acres)
1841	Tower Hamlets	13ha (33acres)

These new cemeteries provided marvellous opportunities for lavish planting schemes. John Loudon's idea of a parkland arboretum was taken up at the Nonconformist garden cemetery, Abney Park Cemetery, in Stoke Newington.

Plants for Abney Park Cemetery

In 1839 George Loddiges became a shareholder of the newly formed Abney Park Cemetery Company and gained the board's acceptance for an ambi-

View of Abney Park Cemetery c.1860

tious planting scheme. He proposed a model arboretum for the cemetery, based on the Nursery's existing arboretum a mile-and-a-half to the south. The arboretum opened in May 1840, just ahead of John Loudon and Joseph Strutt's more publicised Derby Arboretum. When it opened, two thousand tree and shrub species were already in place. Only the magnolia and rhododendron shrubs and additional American beds remained to be stocked that Autumn. John Loudon observed:

> In the Abney Park Cemetery ... a named arboretum has been planted by Messrs Loddiges, which contained every hardy tree and shrub, varieties as well as species, that was in their collection a year ago. The names are on brick, the same as in the Hackney arboretum [of Loddiges].[147]

Here was 'a complete arboretum, including all the hardy kinds of rhododendrons, azaleas and roses in Messrs Loddiges' collection; and in which also dahlias, geraniums, fuchsias, verbenas, petunias, etc, are planted out in patches in the summer season.'[148] For some years it was unrivalled as the largest collection of named trees and shrubs in Britain outside of Loddiges Nursery.

Plants supplied for commerce

Whereas most of the trees and shrubs which were bought from Loddiges Nursery were acquired by collectors and enthusiasts, a small number were bought by commercial concerns. In 1825, and for a few years before and after, attempts were made

to introduce the culture of silk into England and Ireland. It was chiefly through Loddiges Nursery that trees of the most widely used variety of White Mulberry *Morus alba italica* were imported from the continent.[149]

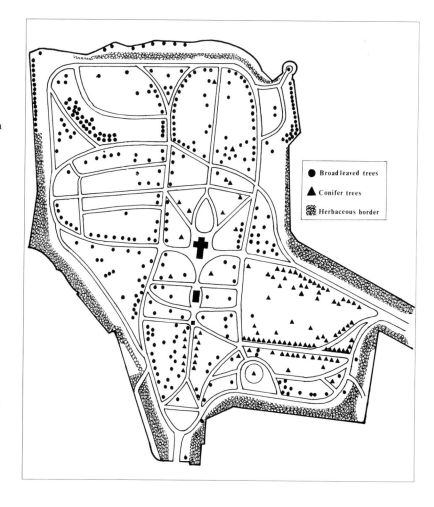

The Abney Park Cemetery Arboretum planted by George Loddiges in 1840 as the largest tree collection in Britain outside their Nursery

Broad leaved trees

Conifer trees

Herbaceous border

CHAPTER SIX
🌿George Loddiges' scientific interests

Many of the achievements of the Nursery are credited to George Loddiges (1786–1846). Although he was the younger of the two sons he achieved the greater prominence in scientific circles. He was elected a Fellow of four learned societies: the [Royal] Microscopical Society, the Zoological Society of London, the [Royal] Horticultural Society and the Linnean Society.[150] He was to serve as a Vice-President of the Horticultural Society, and a council member of the Microscopical Society.

Scientific meetings were hosted at George Loddiges' centrally-heated house in the Nursery grounds.[151] Dr Benjamin Clarke, in *Glimpses of Ancient Hackney and Stoke Newington* (1894) recalled the drawing-room, as observed whilst attending one of Dr John Pye-Smith's geological lectures there:

> The drawing room was warmed, like the hot-houses, by steam pipes, its walls covered with paintings of value by great and well-known masters; at each corner were cases of humming-birds, stuffed, classified and arranged by his own hand, as nearly like to life as could be effected – birds, their nests, their eggs, and even young broods.

The house also contained a chamber organ by the famous Father Smith, that 'would delight the more music-loving company'.

The founding of the Royal Microscopical Society (1839)

The name of George Loddiges is associated with the Royal Microscopical Society due to his role as one of its founders.[152] The society continues to this day and recently celebrated its 150th anniver-

George Loddiges (1786–1846) from a portrait at the Royal Horticultural Society

sary. In the UK this occasion was marked by the issue of commemorative postage stamps.[153]

George Loddiges and six others formed the founding committee of the society. Amongst its initial membership of seventeen, were a number of close friends of George Loddiges. These included Nathaniel Ward, with whom George had worked to promote glass fern cases, and the botanical author and lecturer George William Francis FLS (1800–65), who attended the meetings with George and his son Conrad.

The founding of the Microscopical Society in 1839 was stimulated by the development of new lens technology. The Quaker merchant Joseph Jackson Lister of Stoke Newington had perfected his lens system between 1824–30, in recognition of which he was elected a Fellow of the Royal Society in 1832.[154] Optical instrument-makers did not take up his construction techniques immediately, and when the Society was founded, there were only a few enthusiasts, such as George Loddiges, who had commissioned such lenses for their microscopes.

Fifty years after George Loddiges' death, a

Loddiges Plover-crest **Cephalepsis loddigesi** *Gould. This was the first humming-bird ever named and described in scientific literature by John Gould. Courtesy of the Trustees of the Natural History Museum*

president of the Royal Microscopical Society acknowledged the role of the founding members in the society's history. George Loddiges was described as 'one of the most liberal patrons and most skilful users of the early achromatic objectives'.[155]

Loddigesia mirabilis.
Courtesy of the Trustees of the Natural History Museum

The largest humming-bird collection in Europe

George Loddiges was equally renowned as a specialist ornithologist. He exchanged scientific information about humming-birds and built up an internationally noted collection of the birds.[156] Two humming-birds were named after him.[157] On his death it was noted that:

> His collection of humming birds, which has a great European reputation, is unique. It contains more than 200 species in all stages of plumage and age … [a] larger collection than could be furnished by all the museums of Europe put together.[158]

Humming-birds, their taxidermy and classification, were occupations in which George Loddiges was involved for twenty years.[159] Part of his collection, acquired from a descendant in 1933 along with his catalogue and notes, is now preserved at the British Museum of Natural History, Tring.

When Loddiges Nursery was founded in the mid-eighteenth century, only eighteen species of humming-bird had been scientifically named. By the time the first great illustrated book on humming-birds was published in 1829, this had risen to 110 species.[160] A further illustrated book appeared in 1833, and its scope would have been greatly extended had its illustrator been granted access to George Loddiges unrivalled collection. George Loddiges held back from such an arrangement, planning to secure as many specimens as he could and publish his own magnificent folio.[161]

Had this project come to fruition, George Loddiges would have become a household name. Unfortunately, he died on 5 June 1846, after a long and painful illness. The project was left to the able zoologist

and more skilful artist, John Gould.[162] As a result, Gould became the famous 'Humming-bird Man' of the period. His magnificent coloured plates of Loddiges' birds and those in his own collection, brought their beauty to the appreciation of the wider public, particularly after he secured

Lesbia gouldi.
Courtesy of the Trustees of the Natural History Museum

a position for their display at the Great Exhibition of 1851.

From the late 1820s onwards Gould had developed a close friendship with George Loddiges. He wrote:

> This gentleman and myself were imbued with a kindred spirit in the love we both entertained for this family of living gems. To describe the feeling which animated us with regard to them is impossible. It can, in fact, only be realised by those who have made natural history a study, and who peruse the investigation of its charming mysteries with ardour and delight.[163]

At a Zoological Society meeting in 1830, Gould honoured George Loddiges by naming a new species of humming-bird after him: *Cephalepsis loddigesi* Gould. George, in turn, named a humming-bird after John Gould: *Lesbia gouldi*. It was natural that after George Loddiges' death, his lifelong dream of illustrating his humming-birds in a folio volume, would be brought to fruition by his friend Gould. Those magical hours of contemplation in which Gould had been granted unhindered access to George's collection, had given him an unrivalled knowledge of the bird's origins and habitats, and by whom, when and where each one had been collected. These birds, together with those in his own collection, were described and illustrated in a five volume *Monograph of the Trochilidae*, the first volume of which appeared three years after George's death.

Included in the book was a plate showing an exquisite trio of Loddiges' Plover-crest *Cephalepsis loddigesi* Gould, and another illustrating the Marvellous Spatuletail *Loddigesia mirabilis*, of which George Loddiges' was the only specimen in a collection before 1880.[164] Three cock birds of the Marvellous Spatuletail were illustrated as they might appear in flight, displaying the remarkable tail spatulas which are clapped together during courtship to emit a sound which can be heard thirty yards away. The unique bird in George's collection from which the illustration had been made, had been named in his honour by Charles Bonaparte, a nephew of Napoleon the Great.[165]

The years of closure (1850-54) and after

George Loddiges died, aged 60 in June 1846, leaving his son Conrad to assist William Loddiges in the running of the Nursery.[166] Three years later, in December, William, aged 73, also died. For Loddiges Nursery the deaths of William and George marked the end of an era.

William Loddiges had no children of his own and the family business passed to George's son, Conrad, aged 28. Almost immediately, the young man started to plan the gradual closure of the Nursery. He shared his father's interest in horti-

culture and science, having been awarded honorary membership of the Agricultural Association of Bavaria in 1846, and having accompanied his father to the founding meetings of the Royal Microscopical Society ten years earlier.[167] Given these talents and interests, the Nursery might well have continued to be a focal point of horticultural excellence, but Conrad had to contend with the pressures of a rapidly changing London.

In the mid-1800s the population of Hackney was growing fast, and land for speculative building was at a premium. The railway had arrived, taking a swathe of land where Dr Silvester's gardens had once been laid-out by Joachim Conrad Loddiges. The village character was rapidly becoming submerged into the new, larger city of the industrial age, with its ever increasing burden of air pollution.

The rising land prices and worsening air quality forced nurseries and market gardens to close, or move further out of London. Some successfully defied this trend and a few even opened in Hackney in the latter half of the nineteenth century. One of these was the Frampton Park Nursery, not far from the site of Loddiges Nursery. This firm remained in business until just before the First World War.[168]

St John-at-Hackney Church Gardens

Both William and George Loddiges died in the late 1840s and were buried in front of St John-at-Hackney church. The deterioration of the churchyard in Victorian times was remedied by a grant from the Metropolitan Public Gardens Association which made possible a re-opening to the public on 3 June 1886. On the death of Conrad Loddiges' son, a small legacy was bequeathed to maintain the imposing family chest tomb and the adjacent headstone to the Creighton family, to whom they were related by marriage. The tomb and headstone are in a well-preserved condition in a prominent position close to the main steps of the parish church of St John-at-Hackney.

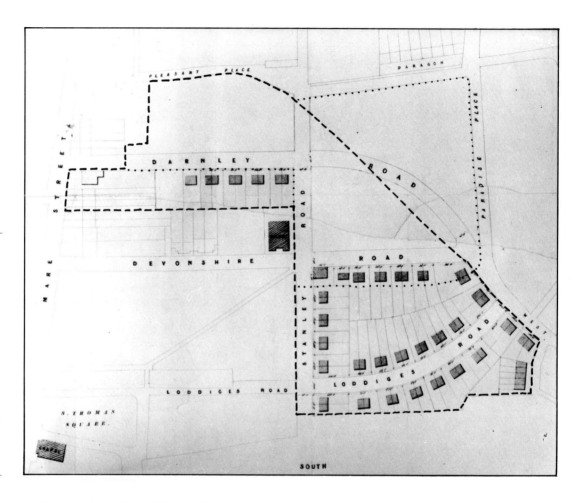

Loddiges' Nursery showing mid-nineteenth century building proposals and new roads on Conrad Loddiges II's Barbers Barn and arboretum field freeholds, integrated with a row of villas on St Thomas' Hospital's land on Devonshire Road. This scheme was not built, a higher density scheme being chosen. Courtesy of the Greater London Record Office

However, for Loddiges Nursery there was an added complication. Its long site lease from St Thomas' Hospital was due to expire on Lady Day 1853, and the governors of St Thomas' Hospital were actively assessing the value of their land in Hackney for building purposes. In 1848, the governors had already prepared a terrier of the hospital's South Hackney holdings, employing Henry Curry as surveyor. They intended to turn their attention to their land north of Well Street in the near future, and began at this date by making a survey of proposed road alignments. From 1848 onwards there were proposals for Darnley, Loddiges, Stanley and Devonshire Roads, the building of which would replace Loddiges Nursery.[169] The family reconciled itself to the changing pattern of society. William Loddiges began to lay plans for the gradual closure of the Nursery, and within a month of his death, his nephew Conrad re-opened discussions with potential purchasers.[170]

It was no small task. The stock was huge and Conrad was determined that the prize plants should stay in Britain if possible, ideally in a collection accessible to both scientists and the general public. In order to achieve this, Conrad was prepared to forego their full sale price. In January 1850 he made a generous offer to William J. Hooker, Director of the Royal Botanic Gardens, Kew, inviting the purchase of the palm collection at one third of its value. Unfortunately William Hooker could no more afford the magnificent collection in 1850 than he could in 1846 when William Loddiges had made him a similar offer.[171]

1851 was a census year, and the census books provide a glimpse of the Loddiges family at home. We learn that Conrad Loddiges, aged 29, employed eleven staff in the nursery and occupied No.1 Loddiges Place with Susannah, aged 32, and their three children aged 6, 5, and 3, and two servants. Conrad's widowed aunt Alice, aged 65, still lived next door at the Nursery's main lodge (where her husband William had died), alone but for one servant. Conrad's mother Jane, 64, lived at Loddiges House, Paradise Field where her husband George had died. With Jane lived her American-born niece Eliza and Conrad's sister Helena, aged 30.[172]

1851 was also the year of the Great Exhibition

Crystal Palace 1851

in Hyde Park.[173] Conrad Loddiges personally arranged the palms for the exhibition, and provided ferns for an exhibition of Wardian Cases displayed jointly by his brother-in-law Edward Cooke and Nathaniel Ward. The latter won an 1851 Great Exhibition Bronze Exhibitor's Medal.

In 1852 the final sale of nursery stock was put in the hands of the auctioneer J.C. Stevens, who advertised it in *The Gardener's Chronicle* on 22 May. All that summer plants were potted-up and sold.[174] That September all the remaining stock was acquired by Sir Joseph Paxton for the Crystal Place Company at Sydenham.[175]

Paxton's most famous purchase was something of a publicity coup. For the opening of the new Crystal Palace at Sydenham, he had bought a palm tree as tall as a three-storey house. It required thirty-two horses to pull it through the streets of London! This amazing sight attracted great crowds and was featured in the *Illustrated London News*.[176] The colossal palm in question was a Mauritius fan palm *Latania borbonica* which

weighed fifteen tons, including its soil and roots.[177] For many years this fan palm had been the gem of Loddiges' collection. It had been acquired in 1814 as a small tree, barely five feet in stature, having previously been at Fontainebleau Palace, in the collection of the Empress Josephine.[178]

The palm was not transported from the Grand Palm House at Loddiges Nursery until July 1854, a year after the expiry of the St Thomas' Hospital lease.[179] It seems likely that the hospital authorities were not keen to repossess the nursery property until their plans for housing development were ready. The sale of the nursery buildings took place on 17 August 1854. Edward Cooke noted in his diary for that day that 1,000,000 bricks were sold, along with other

Giant Fan Palm being pulled through the streets of London by 32 horses. It was sold to the Crystal Palace Company on the closure of Loddiges Nursery. Courtesy of the Illustrated London News

materials and nursery equipment.[180]

The building of Loddiges Road began in 1858 and work on Darnley Road started two years later. Henry Curry based the alignment of Darnley Road on Loddiges' famous linear Camellia House, the route passing through the garden and orchard of the first house in Richmond Terrace (Spackman's Buildings). This house was occupied by Dr Benjamin Clarke, later a noted local historian and author of *Glimpses of Ancient Hackney and Stoke Newington*. Clarke's neighbour, soon to be separated by Darnley Road, was Conrad Loddiges, who now lived in the house which had belonged to his aunt. The building had formerly been the main entrance lodge of the Nursery. Conrad's house, being on the family's freehold, was spared, but Loddiges House at Paradise Field lay directly on the alignment of Frampton Park Road.[181] Clarke's house with its distinctive bay window still stands on the north corner of Darnley Road and Mare Street, but Conrad's house on the opposite corner has been replaced by an office building.

The construction of some of the roads required parts of Conrad Loddiges' freehold. Agreement for the alignment of these roads had to be reached between the hospital's surveyor and Conrad. Conrad then joined other public trustees as a party to the dedication of the new thoroughfares which were named Conrad and Loddiges Roads.[182]

Following the Nursery's closure, Conrad maintained an amateur interest in horticulture, and in 1857 his flowers were awarded a certificate at a

Office building on Mare Street in 1990. Once the site of Conrad Loddiges' house at the main entrance to the Nursery

Conrad Loddiges died in 1865, widely respected in his community. Nearly thirty years later, his former neighbour Dr Benjamin Clarke described him in moving terms as:

> a man of rare endowments and wondrous parts. He lived just long enough to secure the love and respect of a wide circle of friends, and, too early for us, passed away; but his memory is dear to many yet, and not least to myself.[185]

Site of the Grand Palm House in 1990. Today, the Hackney Free and Parochial School occupies the site of the Grand Palm House, once the largest 'tropical rainforest' in Europe

show in Manchester. He continued to grow a range of plants in the garden and greenhouses that lay along Darnley Road, behind the former entrance lodge which he now occupied.[183] However, conditions were not ideal, and in September 1856 he gave 174 orchids to Kew, and donated more two years later.

At about this time Conrad was also a trustee of Hackney's Spurstowe Charity, a charity named after Dr William Spurstowe, a seventeenth-century Nonconformist divine and Vicar of Hackney.[184]

Conrad Loddiges was buried in his wife's vault (Bowes family) in the Nonconformist garden cemetery of Abney Park, Stoke Newington, where his father had once created an arboretum. Conrad's house remained in the family until the death of his son Conrad in 1898, when the property and its contents were auctioned by trustees.[186]

The twentieth century

Of the once great nursery only the name Loddiges Road remains today. Even the Victorian housing pattern which was established on the nursery land has disappeared. The landlord for much of Loddiges Nursery – St Thomas' Hospital – is remembered by the naming of St Thomas' Square, now preserved under the London Squares Preservation Act 1931.

The County of London Plan drawn up in 1943 by Abercrombie and Forshaw proposed new open space on part of the former nursery site. A small corner park has been produced, but the majority of the former nursery land is occupied by public housing and roads. The site of the once famous hothouses is presently occupied by the Hackney Free and Parochial Secondary School and by Darnley Road. For a twentieth-century visitor, it is hard to visualise the Grand Palm House, once the largest indoor 'rain forest' in the world with magnificent palms, ferns and orchids.

In January 1988, George Leslie Loddiges, the last of the male line, died at Bexhill-on-sea.[187] His widow, Mrs Irene C.B. Loddiges, moved to a rest home, and auctioned the family copies of *The Botanical Cabinet* together with one hundred and fifty original water-colours of plants drawn by members of the Loddiges family.[188] She donated original certificates of local historic interest to Hackney Archives Department.

Three remaining houses in Loddiges Terrace, 1994

APPENDIX
❧ *The family & family tree*

Genealogical information about the various generations of the family from the mid-eighteenth century to the present day, has been provided by Marjorie Loddiges, the only descendant still bearing the Loddiges name. Particular interest attaches to George Loddiges' son-in-law, Edward Cooke, whose close involvement with the Nursery and marriage into the Loddiges family is described more fully below. Brief details are also provided of the family connections with the local parish church, the Nonconformist garden cemetery of Abney Park, and the Methodists.

Edward Cooke and Jane Loddiges

The Loddiges and Cookes were close families, both descended from German émigrés.[189] The wives of George and William Loddiges acted as godmothers to two of George Cooke's children. George Cooke's third child, Edward Cooke, married George Loddiges' daughter Jane in January 1840. Their first child, Florence Ada Cooke, died in infancy, aged 18 months and Jane Loddiges died the following year in childbirth. The sickly infant survived only briefly. At the time George Loddiges wrote: 'Poor Mr Cooke bears it better than I could have expected … the infant … is very ill'.[190]

Edward Cooke was born in Pentonville in 1811, but before 1818 he and his father George, the noted marine engraver, had moved to No. 4 Loddiges Place. This was one of the houses built by Joachim Conrad Loddiges to replace Barbers Barn. George Cooke had been offered a long-term commission to engrave the 2,000 copper plates required for *The Botanical Cabinet*. At an early age, Edward Cooke also displayed artistic talent. Before he was nine he was engaged to engrave several thousand plant illustrations onto wood, using specimens from Loddiges Nursery. These were printed as tiny illustrations in John Loudon's *Encyclopaedia of Plants*. Edward Cooke later painted 400 water-colours of Loddiges' plants and his father engraved these onto copper plates for *The Botanical Cabinet*.

As a teenager in the 1820s Edward Cooke concentrated on sketching boats, anchors, fishing-tackle, and the London docks. There followed a brief interlude of architectural studies, before a return to etching ships and boats. On New Year's Day 1829 the famous artist J.S. Cotman was staying with the Cookes, and visited Loddiges Nursery where 'he sketched some of the palms'. Three weeks later, Cooke noted that: 'Mr Loddiges brought us a very difficult plant from the palm house to draw and then engrave for *The Botanical Cabinet*'.

In May 1829, the Cooke family moved to Albion House, Barnes, in south London which was landscaped using plants supplied by Loddiges Nursery.[191] George Cooke died a few years later, not long after the publication of his final plate for *The Botanical Cabinet*.

In 1840 Edward Cooke married Jane Loddiges. During their brief marriage (1840–3), Cooke became interested in ferns and ferneries and illustrated Nathaniel Ward's book on ferns and Wardian Cases published in 1842. One of Edward Cooke's sisters married into the Ward family, giving still closer links between the Cooke, Loddiges, and Ward families. After his wife's death in 1843, Cooke became an authority on ferns. The Ferns, his new London home in Kensington, to which he moved in 1849, had a design of ferns and ferneries worked in metal into the front gate. In 1851, Cooke assisted Ward with the display of Conrad Loddiges' ferns exhibited in Wardian Cases at the Great Exhibition.

Today, Cooke is best remembered as the land-

St John-at-Hackney Church. Tomb of Conrad and Sarah Loddiges, their daughter Sarah and sons George and William and their wives Jane and Alice Creighton. Also George and Jane's daughters Helena and Jane, and Jane's daughter by Edward Cooke, Florence Ada

scape architect for the Victorian gardens of Biddulph Grange in Staffordshire. The estate was owned by the orchid expert James Bateman, an admirer of George Loddiges.[192] The gardens at Biddulph Grange are said to be one of the greatest Victorian gardens in the country, and since 1989 they have been opened to the public by the National Trust.

St John-at-Hackney Church. Headstone to Alice and her husband, Rev. James Creighton, Methodist minister, the parents of Alice and Jane Creighton who married George and William Loddiges

Family links with the Parish Church and with the Methodists

There is no firm evidence concerning the religious affiliations of Joachim Conrad Loddiges and Sarah Aldous, but their family developed strong links with the Methodists. Recent generations have been members of the Church of England. We know that George, William and Conrad allowed friends from the parish church to view the botanic gardens on Sunday afternoons. On Good Fridays, when the camellias were at their best, their friends at the Wesleyan Chapel in Pleasant Place were given an open invitation.[193]

The Methodist connections included matrimonial alliances between the Loddiges and the Rentons, Creightons, and Fawcett-Pyles. Between them, these families produced two Methodist Ministers and the illustrator of *The Methodist Magazine*. Family burials took place at the parish church of St John-at-Hackney and at Abney Park Cemetery.

Burials at St John-at-Hackney

Joachim Conrad Loddiges (1738–1826)
Sarah Loddiges née Aldous (1740–1815)
George Loddiges (1786–1846)
Jane Loddiges née Creighton (1812–43)
William Loddiges (1776–1849)
Alice Loddiges née Creighton (1785–1858)
Sarah Loddiges (1778–1836)
Miss Helena Loddiges (1817–71)
Florence Ada Cooke (1841–2)

All buried at St John-at-Hackney churchyard in the family vault.

Rev. James Creighton
(1738–1819)
Alice Creighton
(1746–1816)
Buried at St John-at-Hackney churchyard beneath the Creighton headstone.

Burials at Abney Park Cemetery

Conrad Loddiges II
(1821–65)
Buried at Abney Park Cemetery in the Bowes family vault, Dr Watt's Walk.

Evelyn Pyle née Loddiges (1844–93)
Buried at Abney Park Cemetery in the Pyle family vault.

Abney Park Cemetery. Tomb of Conrad Loddiges II (1821–65), the last of the Nursery managers

Abney Park Cemetery. Granite memorial to Pyle family including Evelyn Pyle, née Loddiges (1844–93), daughter of Conrad Loddiges II, and her husband Rev. James Fawcett-Pyle, Wesleyan minister

Caspar Burchart LODDIGES
1694/5–Jun.1770

Joachim Conrad LODDIGES
bpt. 9 Oct. 1738–13 Mar. 1826
m. 5 Dec. 1769
Sarah ALDOUS
b.1740–3 Dec. 1815
Both bd. Loddiges family vault St John-at-Hackney

Wilhelmina Amalia LODDIGES
bpt. 13 Dec. 1739
m. 7 Feb. 1774
Ludwig HASE

Sophia Charlotte LODDIGES
b. 11 Oct. 1744
bd. 7 Feb. 1745

William
LODDIGES
b. 6 Jul. 1770–
20 Sep. 1774

Mary
LODDIGES
b. 20 Jul. 1773–
17 Dec. 1778

m. (1) 22 Feb. 1808
Sophia MULLIS
b. 1777–6 Jul. 1810
ISSUE

William LODDIGES
b. 5 Jul. 1776–28 Dec. 1849
m. (2) 17 Oct 1811 same day as George
Alice CREIGHTON
b. 6 Aug. 1785–3 Jan. 1858
Alice & Wm. bd. Loddiges family vault
St John-at-Hackney.
ISSUE: Maria m. 12 Oct. 1837 Edward HUGHES

Jane LODDIGES
b. 30 Jul. 1812–28 Dec. 1843
m. 13 Jun. 1840
Edward William COOKE RA FRS FZS FGS FSA
b. 27 Mar. 1811–1 Jan. 1880
ISSUE: Florence Ada b. 17 Mar. 1841–11 Sep. 1842
Jane and Florence bd. Loddiges family vault St John-at-Hackney

Helena LODDIGES
b. 2 Oct. 1817–15 Feb. 1871
bd. Loddiges family vault
St John-at-Hackney

Evelyn LODDIGES
b. 5 May 1844–6 Jun. 1893
m. 7 Jul. 1868
Rev. James Fawcett-Pyle
b. 12 Nov. 1841–13 Jul. 1913
Both buried Fawcett-Pyle family vault
Abney Park Cemetery
ISSUE

Conrad LODDIGES
b. 27 Dec. 1845–11 Aug. 1898
m. 1 Aug. 1878
Henrietta Helena Bradnack ATKINS
b. 17 Mar. 1848–25 Oct. 1927
ISSUE: (1) Helena
b. 4 Dec. 1880–14 Nov. 1975
(2) Conrad MC MRCS LRCP
b. 16 Aug. 1882–22 Jun. 1949

Loddiges family tree

* also two brothers: Georg Christoph, b. Braekel, alive in 1754; and Ferdinand, b. Segeste, alive in 1757

bold names: family members involved most closely with horticulture and the Nursery

underlined names: lineage of Loddiges surname to the present day

m. **Maria Magdalene***
1718–90

Johanna Dorothea LODDIGES	Maria Margaretha LODDIGES	Johann Georg LODDIGES	Johanna Heinrietta LODDIGES
b. 11 Oct. 1744	bpt. 4 Jun. 1749	bpt. 23 Jun. 1754	bpt. 15 Apr. 1757
bd. 22 Feb. 1750	(died same day)	bd. 17 Apr. 1755	bd. 1 May 1757

Sarah
LODDIGES
b. 10 Jul. 1778–
6 Jul. 1836
bd. Loddiges vault
St John-at-Hackney

Mary
LODDIGES
b. 16 Nov. 1782–
24 Oct. 1798

George
LODDIGES FLS FZS FHS FMS
b. 12 Mar. 1786–5 Jun. 1846
m. 17 Oct. 1811 same day as Wm.
Jane CREIGHTON
b. 24 Mar. 1787– 18 Jul. 1859
Both bd. Loddiges vault St John-at-Hackney

Conrad LODDIGES
b. 14 Apr. 1821–20 Jan. 1865
m. 14 Jun. 1842
Susanna Agar BOWES
b. 21 Sept. 1819–8 Mar. 1897
Both bd. Bowes family vault Abney Park Cemetery

George LODDIGES
b. 13 Apr. 1847–22 Apr. 1923
m. 18 Jul. 1871
Caroline Emily Pykes ATKINS
b. 20 Dec. 1849–22 Jul. 1933

Laelia LODDIGES
b. 10 May 1872–24 Feb. 1948
m. 10 Mar. 1903
Francis William BOWES
NO ISSUE

George Bowes LODDIGES
b. 31 May 1873–4 Feb. 1935
m. 30 Nov. 1901
Bertha Constance HILL
b. 27 Jul. 1869–29 Jan. 1953

Oenone Emily LODDIGES
b. 8 Jan. 1876–12 Feb. 1947
m. 5 Aug. 1899
Henry OERTLING
b. 29 Feb. 1848–19 Dec. 1921
ISSUE

George Leslie LODDIGES
b. 30 Nov. 1902–22 Jan. 1988
m. Irene C.B. HILLIER
b. 26 Feb 1909

Marjorie Bertha LODDIGES
b. 23 Aug. 1907

Abbreviations used in the footnotes

BA British Association
GLRO Greater London Record Office
J. Hort. Soc. *Journal of the Horticultural Society*
J. Royal Mic. Soc. *Journal of the Royal Microscopical Society*
H.A.D. Hackney Archives Department
Pers. comm. personal communication
PRO Public Record Office
Proc. Linn. Soc. *Proceedings of the Linnean Society*
Trans. Royal Hort. Soc. *Transactions of the Royal Horticultural Society*

1 John Harvey, *Early Nurserymen* (1974).

2 John Harvey, item in *Garden History Society Newsletter*, 1988, No. 23, p. 10.

3 Busch is known to have been a German émigré. His name is spelt 'Busch' or 'Bush'. His family pedigree and an accurate year of birth as well as his date of arrival and settlement in England are still not researched. Records of baptisms and marriages are held at GLRO. The first mention of Busch in Hackney occurs in 1756. He is first mentioned in the Poor Rate records for Church/Mare Street in 1756 (P/J/P/110) confirmed by the Statute Labour & Composition Books (P/J/H/36). 1757 is the earliest date in the Church Rate records for Busch leasing land in Church/Mare Street (it was previously leased to Thomas Pells). Anthony Cross 'Russian Gardens, British Gardeners' *Garden History*, (1991) 19 Pt. 1, makes a reference to the arrival of Busch in England in 1744, the date given on the memorial plaque formerly at Isleworth Church.

Busch would have been quite young at this date. Note: most parish records are anglicised to 'Bush'.

4 There currently appears to be no published or unpublished research except for Marcus Kohler, *Die Gartenkunst* (1993), pp. 101–25. Regarding the plant, it is still one of three *Ledum* species generally cultivated in our gardens. Its introduction by Busch is noted in John Loudon *Arboretum et Fruticetum Britannicum* (1838), vol. 1, p. 82.

5 Princess Augusta (d.1772), the daughter-in-law of George II, began her Kew collection in the 1750s. A Maidenhair tree or *Ginkgo biloba* is the oldest surviving tree. It was planted in 1762. The sale of plants to Princess Augusta of Kew Palace is mentioned in J. Harvey, *Early Gardening Catalogues* (1972), p. 49, which refers to an original source [Royal Archives 55512].

6 Edmund and Dorothy Berkeley, *Correspondence of John Bartram 1734–1777* (USA 1992).

7 Anthony Cross, 'The English Garden in Catherine the Great's Russia' *Journal of Garden History*, 1993, vol. 13, No. 3 July–Sept, pp. 172–81. Anthony Cross 'Catherine the Great and the English Garden' in *New Perspectives on Russian and Soviet Artistic Culture*. Fourth World Congress for Soviet and East European Studies, (1990).

8 Brown and Kent's work at Stowe was a favourite of Catherine's and several of its architectural features were copied almost like-for-like. Peter Hayden 'The Russian Stowe' *Garden History*, 1991, vol. 19, No. 1.

9 Vincent Cronin *Catherine, Empress of all Russia* (1989), and Anthony Cross, 'Russian Gardens, British Gardeners' *Garden History*, (1991) vol. 19, 1991, No. 1, pp. 12–20.

10 Approximate translation from the French – e.g. Harold Carter, *Sir Joseph Banks and the Plant Collection from Kew sent to the Empress Catherine II of Russia 1795* (1974), p. 5. Busch and Sparrow were but two of many 'English-style' gardeners who worked in Russia from the 1770s until well into Alexander I's reign. They were the earliest, and hence were the first to introduce many new features, including gravel walks. Amongst others were James Meader, a Scot recruited from the Duke of Northumberland's Syon Park in London and employed by Catherine in 1779/80 to work at Peterhof in the Gulf of Finland. There may have been a connection between Meader and Busch because Busch was to retire to Syon Park. Other Scots included Francis Reid and John Munro, who signed four year contracts in 1782 to work at a palace near Moscow. Others, such as William Gould, worked for Russian aristocrats, although Gould was later employed by Catherine, after the death of his patron in 1791.

11 John Loudon, (1850), q.v. Isobel Rae, *Charles Cameron: architect to the Court of Russia* (1971).

12 The Tsarskoe Selo garden was about four miles in circumference and still had the original 'Dutch' garden with 'fish canals, avenues, neat bowers, alleys, espaliers and close boskets with mossy seats'. It was this style that Catherine wanted Busch to alter.

13 By 1780 Catherine had appointed an assistant for John Busch, a Scot named John McLaren [see Anthony Cross, 'Russian Gardens, British Gardeners' *Garden History*, (1991), vol. 19, No. 1, pp. 12–20].

14 It is said that Busch travelled with his wife, four daughters and son Joseph Charles [Isobel Rae, (1971), *op. cit.*, p. 41]. Busch married the aptly named Ann Plant in about 1752. Baptism records for St John-at-Hackney before their departure show only three daughters, Mary Busch (bap. 31/10/1756), Ann Busch (bap. 6/5/1759) and Catherine Busch (bap. 23/4/1765). Besides Joseph Charles Busch (bap. 7/12/1760), John and Ann Busch had two other sons, James Thelman Busch (bap. 12/12/1762) and John Busch (bap. 24/11/1754). John, the eldest son, stayed behind in Hackney to marry Elizabeth Simpson of the same parish on 2/5/1771. The only other Busch records for the parish are i) a marriage record for an Edward Busch 17/7/1735; ii) a marriage record for a George Busch to Mary Ruddel 15/9/1795; iii) a marriage record for a James Busch to Sarah Smith 19/12/1813. Further research would be required to construct the family tree, and clarify whether these belong to the same Busch family [All records at GLRO]. After John Busch's return from Russia and burial at Isleworth Church, there is a burial record for a John Busch at St John-at-Hackney 10/2/1799 aged 68, hence there was at least one other Busch family in the parish of St John in the late eighteenth century.

15 Dr Thomas Dimsdale inoculated the Empress against smallpox in 1768. He was created a Baron by the Empress. Elizabeth visited the Busch family in 1781 when her husband was inoculating the Empress' grandsons. She records in her diary 'Had a good English dinner. Mrs Busch and four daughters agreeable people … Busch was paid a yearly salary of 19,000 rubles; he had several hundred citrus trees to care for; he produced excellent fruit, and Mrs Busch fattened turkeys on dried ants' eggs.' Anthony Cross, *An English Lady at the Court of Catherine the Great: the journal of Baroness Elizabeth Dimsdale 1781* (1981).

16 Anthony Cross, 'Russian Gardens, British Gardeners' *Garden History*, (1991), vol. 19, No. 1 pp. 12–20.

17 Isobel Rae, (1971), *op.cit.*

18 Brumheld, *A History of Russian Architecture* (1993), p. 281. Cameron's landscaping work took place in

the last seventeen years of Catherine's reign (1779–96). For further information see: Victor & Audrey Kennett, *The Palaces of Leningrad* (1976). In 1795, the year before the Empress died, George III commanded Sir Joseph Banks to send a select consignment of plants to Pavlovsk. The plants were sent from Kew Palace's stove house and Cape House [ref: Harold Carter, (1974), *op.cit.*].

19 The date of the wedding is believed to have been 1784 [ref: Anthony Cross, 'Russian Gardens, British Gardeners' *Garden History*, (1991), vol. 19, No. 1, p. 19].

20 Anthony Cross, 'Russian Gardens, British Gardeners' *Garden History*, (1991), vol. 19. No. 1.

21 In the article (*Horticultural Transactions*, (1821), IV) Joseph Busch is styled 'Gardener to His Imperial Majesty the Emperor of Russia'. The following year (1822) Joseph Busch is styled C.M.H.S. (Certificate of Merit of the Horticultural Society) by John Loudon, *Encyclopaedia of Gardening* (1822).

22 The exact date of death is not recorded. These were perilous times in Russia. Napoleon invaded Russia in June and entered Moscow in September.

23 J. Silvester-Davies, 'The Loddiges of Hackney' *Athenaeum*, (1899), 25 Feb, p. 245.

24 This section of the letter was written in Jeremiah's handwriting [ref: Spriggs, *Collected Correspondence of Jeremy Bentham Vol. 2 1777–80*, (1968)]. Unfortunately, prior to 1781 Hackney St John Land Tax records do not list landlords and there is no later record of Bentham as a lessor of land to Busch. Bentham's ownership of Busch's nursery land is not made clear in his will of 1792 (PRO) which only refers to Hackney in connection with his role as Receiver for the Cass Estate. However it may be in this context that the land was leased. Some of Bentham's rental records are available (BM Mss No. 37336) but these also offer no help. The Benthams are known to have been involved with property speculation and investment and Isobel Rae, *Charles Cameron: architect to the Court of Russia* (1971), p. 41. writes that Jeremiah held Busch in high regard. Samuel Bentham is likely to have had some interest in Busch's work in Tsarskoe Selo due to his own work on Potemkin's estate of Krichev in Belorussia. John Aiton, nephew of the King's Gardener at Kew, had been recruited by Jeremy Bentham to work with Samuel at this estate – Anthony Cross, 'Russian Gardens, British Gardeners' *Garden History*, (1991) vol. 19, No. 1, pp. 12–20.

25 Isobel Watson (1989) *Gentlemen in the Building Line: the development of South Hackney* (1989), p.81. On the Cass Estate one road is named Bentham Road (roads in the northern parts were given names after past treasurers). Discovery of the site used by Busch and Loddiges may be difficult due to under-letting and assignment of Cass leases during the currency of the principal lease with no requirement to notify the trustees of these until the mid-1800s [ref: Isobel Watson *op.cit.*, p. 59].

26 John Loudon *Arboretum et Fruticetum Britannicum* (1838), vol. 1, p. 83, [records Busch as having introduced the flowering currant *Ribes diacantha*, the Grey Alder tree *Alnus incana*, and the shrubs: *Caragana jubata* and *Rhododendron chrysanthemum*, between 1780 and 1800]. Busch appears in the Isleworth rate books for 1789–91. His burial is recorded at All Saints, Isleworth on 22/5/1795.

27 Hackney Archives Department M196 (1848) refers to the surrender in 1815 by Joseph Busch – (roughly on the site of today's Graham Road properties) of the site of a messuage (building and garden) on the west side of Church/ Mare Street. This property, lying on the west side of the brook, had been pulled down and added to Mr R. Dann's courtyard. To the north of it lay a messuage (garden & stable) surrendered to Dann by Thomas Saville in 1821 and converted into offices.

28 George Loddiges, *The Botanical Cabinet*, vol. 17, plate 1628.

29 Busch's nursery is erroneously presumed to have been on the east side of Church/Mare Street at Loddiges' later Barbers Barn site by at least two authors. Although its exact locations remain unclear its several sites are recorded on the west side of Church/Mare Street in the Land Tax, Church Rate and Poor Rate records.

30 It is clear that land formerly belonging to Busch in Church/Mare Street was assigned within a year or so of his departure to Arnold. This is shown by the entries for Lamp Rate in 1772 and the Church Rate in 1774. A remark in the Highways Rate ledger for 1774 implies that Busch may have left this land with Conrad Loddiges as agent to sell on to a buyer such as Arnold. A further site belonging to Busch (acquired from Newton) was also not transferred to Conrad Loddiges for continuation of the nursery, but assigned to John Field. There is a deed for this dated 22/6/1771 and held in the GLRO (MDR/1771/3/442) in which Busch endorses an old unexpired lease, originally between Mary Newton & John Tinsley, in which he appears to have held the interest since 1768. Busch 'assigns of John Tinsley to John Field all land for the duration of the lease'.

31 Conrad Loddiges' father was Casper Buchart (=Vurhart) Loddiges. His grandfather on his mother's side is believed to have been called Groten.

32 Following the death of the last of the male line, the key family papers were donated in 1988 by the widowed Mrs Irene C.B. Loddiges to Hackney Archives Department. A letter from Conrad Loddiges in the possession of Rev. J. Silvester-Davies (see J. Silvester-Davies, 'The Loddiges of Hackney', Athenaeum, (1899), 25 Feb, p. 245) says that Conrad's father served as a gardener to 'a nobleman', and his grandfather served 'the king' in the royal gardens at Hanover. In 1805 Conrad Loddiges gave his origin as 'Hertzberg in Hanover'

in his UK aliens registration document. His date of baptism is courtesy of the family tree provided by Helena Loddiges.

33 The local commander was Vincent Judes de St Pern. Note: Loddiges is spelt Lochlies in this document [See: Hackney Archives Department, D/F/LOD 1 for full document].

34 His visit to Münster may have been to see relatives since Braekel (birthplace of his uncle Georg Christoph on his mother's side) is in Münster [information provided on family tree by pers. comm. Marjorie Loddiges 13/11/1988].

35 Dated 1 July 1757.

36 This is an approximate translation, made for us by the German Historical Society. The original document was kindly presented to Hackney Archives Department, (D/F/LOD/2) by Mrs Irene C.B. Loddiges (née Hillier) in July 1988, when other family property was auctioned.

37 J. Silvester-Davies, 'The Loddiges of Hackney', Athenaeum, (1899), 25 Feb, p. 245, relates how, in a letter he inherited, Conrad Loddiges 'lapses into Dutch'. This misled some biographers into believing that Conrad Loddiges was Dutch. The date of arrival of Conrad Loddiges in England (1761), his former residence at 'Felzen' (Velzen), and original upbringing at Hertzberg in Hanover are given in his admission for an 1805 Westminster Crown Court Alien Office Permit at Hackney Archives Department, D/F/LOD 3.

38 Silvester had been an army physician in the Low Countries. He had married into a Dutch family, marrying the daughter of a colonel in the Dutch Service. The Silvesters appear to have been of Huguenot origin. They once owned an estate near Bordeaux but they moved first to the Low Countries and then to England to avoid religious persecution. Silvester was elected a Fellow of the Royal Society on 7 May 1747. He was elected whilst serving as physician to the French Protestant

Hospital in Hoxton, London.

39 Isobel Watson, 'Spurstowe's House and Silvester's Garden', *The Hackney Terrier*, (1991/2), Winter Issue; also J. Silvester-Davies, 'The Loddiges of Hackney', *Athenaeum*, (1899) 25 Feb, p. 245, describes Sir John Silvester as 'introducing Loddiges into this country as his gardener'. Information on the family pedigree is available at Hackney Archives Department, M280.

40 Isobel Watson, 'Spurstowe's House and Silvester's Garden', *The Hackney Terrier*, (1991/2), Winter Issue; the house and grounds were bought by a land owning neighbour Mr Richard Dann.

41 Taylor, *Old London Gardens* (1953), from an original quote in John Loudon *Arboretum et Fruticetum Britannicum* (1838), giving a suggested date for the sale to the Marquis of 1758. John Feltwell, *The Naturalist's Garden* (1987), gives 1763 as the date the rhododendron was first introduced into our gardens but it is likely that seed was first grown in a garden in the UK in the previous century. Firm dates for introductions are always difficult to establish. Many plants were introduced to private estate gardens but were not grown by nurseries to avoid the need to introduce fresh seed later.

42 Shirley Hibberd, *Rustic Adornments for Homes of Taste* (1856). Much of this Victorian and the later Edwardian popularity was based on the sale of artificial hybrids rather than the natural species. The first artificial hybrid was not available until 1820. By 1860 over 500 different types were available, partly following Hooker's introduction of examples from the Himalayas in 1849 which led to new hybrids.

43 Leaflets describing the problem associated with *Rhododendron ponticum* can be obtained from the Snowdonia National Park Centre at Plas Tan-y-Bwlch. [Background information is available in M. Shaw, '*Rhododendron ponticum* – ecological reasons for the success of an alien species in Britain and features that may assist in its control', *Aspects of Applied Biology*, (1984), vol. 5, p. 231.

44 J. Silvester-Davies, 'The Loddiges of Hackney', *Athenaeum*, (1899), 25 Feb.

45 The child was born 6/7/1770 (baptism record for William Loddiges, St John-at-Hackney 13/7/70, GLRO).

46 Joachim Conrad Loddiges' early land holdings in Church/Mare Street are first listed in the Church Rate ledger for 1774 (three years after Busch had departed). At this time Loddiges held one piece of land at or near his house. He held a second on which he was paying Church Rate, Poor Rate, and Highways Rate, but this had formerly belonged to Kellaway, not Busch. The 1774 Highways Rate (P/J/H/61), p.17 records 'Kellaway now C. Loddiges by own confession from 18/5/1774.' Loddiges also owned a garden and field south of Milward's land, London Lane.

47 This is quoted from the unpublished local history manuscript HAD M3958 'A few lines relating to the Parish of Hackney' held at Rose Lipman Local History Library, Hackney. The statements in the manuscript are confirmed by Rate book entries for 1774 and thereafter (the Bannister Lane field off Well Street is not specifically confirmed in these records until 1778). The Bannister Lane or Well Street field has to be the one shown on the lease plan and document (GLRO Ref: H1/ST/E67/38/26) for a small field (55ft x 275ft x70ft x 268ft) abutting and south of (hence behind?) St Thomas' Place in Bannister Lane. This field was owned by St Thomas' Hospital, implying that Bannister was the hospital's lessee for this part of their estate (hence Bannister Lane) and the field was in turn rented out to Conrad Loddiges. By 1789 Joachim Conrad Loddiges was the hospital's lessee and Bannister was no longer involved. At this date he re-assigned the field to Mr Ebenezer Johnstone from 21 Jan 1790 until expiry of the lease from the hospital in

1804. The formal lease from the hospital had probably been obtained by Loddiges when Bannister's lease expired in 1783 for a term of 21 years to 1804. This field is the tiny corner curtilage in the south-west corner of Well Street/Bannister Lane. It is still shown abutting St Thomas' Place on Stanford's 1860 map of London, although it has one house in it at that date.

48 John Harvey, 'Mid-Georgian Nurseries of the London Region', *London & Middlesex Archaeological Society Transactions*, (1975), XXVI. The two which predated Loddiges' were by William Malcolm of Kennington in 1771, and by Kennedy & Lee of Hammersmith in 1774.

49 The first edition to include an introduction written in French was published in 1783.

50 Land Tax records at Hackney Archives Department. There was also Conrad Loddiges' informal arrangement with Busch regarding at least one site – Bentham's land (the location of which remains unidentified but is presumed to be part of the Cass Estate).

51 Nathaniel Acton Lee's address was Livermore Park, Suffolk. In the land tax records his name is given as Acton Lee but he later styled himself with Acton as the surname. The site of the seed shop lay between London Lane and the Horse and Groom tavern, in one of a line of red-brick houses probably those shown on John Roque's map of 1741–5 and also on the 1831 St John-at-Hackney Parish Map ['Starling map' reprinted by L.B.H. Archives Dept 1983 ref: M3/2]. The Horse & Groom is shown on John Roque's map and all others including the 'Hackney 1870' Godfrey Edition of reprinted Old Ordnance Survey Maps by which time the seed shop terrace has been demolished, as noted by Benjamin Clarke (1893), p. 32. The Acton family is well researched, and details are available from the Suffolk County Council archivist. The Acton/Acton Lee/Lee Acton freeholds are shown on the 1831 Starling

map. After 1836 the land passed to Nathaniel Acton Lee's sister Dame Harriet Middleton. The properties from London Lane northwards were nos 1–11 Church/Mare Street, beginning at London Lane. Which one of these was Loddiges' seed shop is still not clear, but if one of the properties demolished by Clarke's time, it was probably between nos. 1–5. We can at least trace the site of Loddiges' garden. After no.11 came the Horse and Groom, its garden, yard and passage with a square 'garden' of 1a 0r 16p at its end on its southern end. This plot appears to be Aird's garden in 1826 on the leasehold map HA/93/3/834 at Ipswich County Archive.

52 The fields were bought at an auction held on 22 August 1785 at a cost of £65 2s from assignees of the former lessee (Joseph Spackman) following his bankruptcy. The re-assignment of Spackman's lease to Loddiges was drawn up in March 1786. On the lease document map (St Thomas' Hospital Archive, GLRO) Barbers Barn is already shown as Mr Loddiges' freehold (although it is believed to have been occupied by a lessee owner coming to the end of his lease). These dates are confirmed by Church Rate records. In 1785 Conrad Loddiges paid Church Rates on four sites. The fourth, in Bannister Lane, had been let out. 1786 was the first year when Conrad Loddiges was assessed for Poor Rate on a fifth site – the large Church Street Field (probably 2 acres 1 rod 3 perches), and Seven Acre Field (Paradise Field) (6 acres 2 rods 8 perches). St Thomas' Hospital leases with maps of the Loddiges grounds are held at GLRO (e.g. H1/ST/E67/28/3 3/March/1786).

53 Initially Conrad Loddiges continued to let out or sub-lease the Seven Acre Field to John Abbatt, a corn chandler, thereby honouring the arrangements of his predecessor Joseph Spackman. Indeed he may permanently have let half of this field out, since he did not enclose it into the walled nursery site.

54 1787 is generally given (e.g. HAD M3958 at Hackney Archives Department) as the date when Joachim Conrad Loddiges moved to or opened up the Barbers Barn/Paradise Field site as his nursery. The 1787 date appears to refer to the completion of such works as were required for the opening of the consolidated nursery site for business. By then the site must have been sufficiently secure. [Conrad Loddiges walled and fenced Paradise Field (Hackney Archives Department, HAD M3958). This is also mentioned in Edward Walford, *Old and New London: The Western and Northern Suburbs*, (n/d c.1880). The walled-in boundary took in only the southern triangular half of the field which became the Hackney Botanic Garden perimeter; the remainder was merely re-fenced and continued to be used as a field]. The Seven Acre Field is shown on Milne's Land-use Map as meadow and pasture and Church Street Field as market garden. (Thomas Milne's *Land Use Map of London & Environs in 1800*, London Topographical Society, facsimile reprint 1975/6). The reason Milne does not show any land on Church/Mare Street as a nursery garden appears to be that, at the date of his survey (1795–9), when Loddiges Nursery was in transition, its old growing grounds would have been too small to show and the land which became the Hackney Botanic Garden had only just been acquired and was not secure for laying-out as a nursery garden until 1787.

55 The Hackney Botanic Garden plan/layout was published in John Loudon, *Encyclopaedia of Gardening*, (1834 edn.), para 6904; [and 1850 edition as revised by Jane Loudon, para 6279].

56 The document was presented to the Hackney Archives Department, (D/F/LOD/3) by Irene C.B. Loddiges.

57 John Renton I was buried at St John-at-Hackney churchyard 26 July 1810. He ran the Hoxton Field Nursery between c.1768–92 and thereafter worked

as Head Gardener at Loddiges Nursery. His son, John Renton II drew portraits for *The Methodist Magazine*. His painted portraits of Joachim Conrad Loddiges, George Loddiges and his wife Jane Loddiges were exhibited at the British Institute and the Royal Academy in 1821.

58 William Robinson, *Athenaeum*, (1899), No. 3721, Feb 18, p. 88, says Joachim Conrad Loddiges acquired Barbers Barn in 1792. This was the date of his transactions with John Rowell, and it is assumed that expiry of Rowell's lease under Joachim Conrad Loddiges freehold, and perhaps therefore the ending of use of the building by Worsley's School happened about the same time. Loddiges Place could date from 1792 since the Poor Rate mentions 'new erections'. However these could refer to entrance buildings for the Nursery or Joachim Conrad Loddiges' own house, also built along the freehold frontage. In this case, William Robinson, History and Antiquities of the Parish of Hackney (1842), may be correct in claiming that Barbers Barn was pulled down in 1813.

59 i.e. adjacent to the Royal London Assurance building, 222 Church/Mare Street.

60 Sims, John '*Loddigesia oxalidifolia*', *The Botanical Magazine*, (1807), vol. 24, plate 965.

61 Ibid.

62 Seed of *Loddigesia oxalidifolia* had first been supplied to Joachim Conrad Loddiges by his correspondent George Hibbert. The plants grew wild at The Cape of Good Hope. John Loudon in his *Encyclopaedia of Plants* (1822) gave its date of introduction as 1802.

63 Ibid.

64 'Horticultural History Notes: Pioneer Gardens in North London' *Journal of Horticulture & Cottage Gardening*, (14 May 1896).

65 The Hackney Botanic Nursery Garden and similar titles were used by John Loudon.

66 George Loddiges drew some of the illustrations which were engraved by George Cooke for *The*

Botanical Cabinet. It is widely referred to as George Loddiges' endeavour.

67 From 1821 onwards the leasehold fields held from St Thomas' Hospital came into the ownership of William and George Loddiges. The brothers took the option at this early date to extend them from 1832 until 1853 (or were given this as a joint stake in the business by their father) . The lease documents are held at GLRO (H1/ST/E67/46/19 12/4/1821). At some time before 1821 an additional field was bought freehold. It adjoined the southern end of the Seven Acre Field and became part of the arboretum. After 1821 this land was in the names of Conrad's sons, William and George. Later it passed to Conrad Loddiges II, under whose ownership Loddiges Road was built across the site.

68 These descriptions and events are given by Benjamin Clarke, *Glimpses of Ancient Hackney and Stoke Newington* (1893).

69 Noel Kingsbury, 'Fashion Under Glass', *The Garden*, 1991, p. 298.

70 1788 is given as the date of the earliest experimental steam heated hothouses.

71 David Stuart, *Georgian Gardens* (1799), p. 140.

72 Joseph Sabine 'An Account of a Method of Conveying Water to Plants, in houses, Invented by Mr George Loddiges of Hackney', *Trans. Hort. Soc.*, (1820), III, p.14. Also reported in 'Notices of Communications to the Society' *Trans. Hort. Soc.*, (1821), vol.4. p. 56; and widely described in horticultural histories – e.g. John Loudon, *Encyclopaedia of Gardening* (1850 edn., revisions by Jane Loudon), p.625, and George Chadwick, *The Works of Sir Joseph Paxton 1803–1865* (1961), p. 7.

73 The date of building is unknown but it is shown on the revised leases drawn up from St.Thomas' Hospital in 1821. This is the earliest reference to George Loddiges' house.

74 *Trans. Hort. Soc.*, (1821), vol. IV, p. 56.

75 Ibid.

76 Ibid.

77 Ibid.

78 *op.cit.*, p. 1225.

79 Observations dated 1825 [translated from *Botanische Zeitung* 1825] reported in William J. Hooker [ed.], 'Schultes's Botanical Visit to England', *The Botanical Miscellany*, (1830), vol. 1, p. 48, and an identical but shorter article in John Loudon [ed.], *The Gardener's Magazine*, (1829), vol. 5, p. 308.

80 John Loudon [ed], 'Catalogue of the Different Species of Palms Cultivated in the Stoves of the Hackney Garden', *Gardener's Magazine*, (1826), vol. 1, pp. 136–8.

81 John Loudon [ed.], 'The London Nurseries …', *Gardener's Magazine*, (1830), vol. 6, p. 373.

82 Jacob Rintz, 'Remarks on Various Gardens About London and in other parts of England', *The Gardener's Magazine*, (1829), vol. 5, p. 379.

83 These insectivorous plants are mentioned in 'Calls at London Nurseries: The Hackney Botanic Garden' *The Gardener's Magazine*, (1833) vol. 9, p. 467.

84 Ibid.

85 Joseph Paxton, 'Garden Architecture', *Magazine of Botany*, vol. VIII, p. 255

86 John Loudon, 'The Hackney Botanic Nursery' *Encyclopaedia of Gardening* (1822), p. 1225.

87 Ibid., and Melanie Simo, 'John Claudius Loudon: On Planning and Design for the Garden Metropolis' *Garden History*. (1989) vol. 9, No. 2, p. 184, and Melanie Simo, *Loudon and the Landscape* [USA 1988]. The Camellia House was first described in 1822 [ref: John Loudon, *Encyclopaedia of Gardening* (1822), p. 576].

88 Mary Woods and Arete Warren, *Glasshouses: a History of Greenhouses, Orangeries and Conservatories* (1988).

89 John Loudon, 'The Hackney Botanic Nursery', *Encyclopaedia of Gardening* (1822) p. 1225.

90 John Loudon [ed.], 'Calls at the London Nurseries:

The Hackney Botanic Garden' *The Gardener's Magazine*, (1833), vol. 9, pp. 467–9.

91 Ibid.

92 Extract from William Allen's diary quoted in Desmond Chapman-Huston & Ernest Cripps, *Through a City Archway: the story of Allen and Hanbury's 1715–1954* (1954), p. 279.

93 Ibid. footnote 79.

94 Jacob Rinz, 'Remarks on Various Gardens around London', *Gardener's Magazine*, (1829) vol. 5, p. 379.

95 John Loudon, *Encyclopaedia of Gardening* (1822).

96 This layout was mapped for the second edition of John Loudon *Encyclopaedia of Gardening* (1834 edn.), and was faithfully reproduced after his death in the revised edition produced by Jane Loudon in her 1850 edition.

97 William Robinson, *Athenaeum*, (1899), No. 3721, 18 Feb, p. 214, and Mavis Batey 'Edward Cooke, landscape gardener FRS, FLS, FZS, FZA etc: A Victorian par excellence', *Garden History*, vol. 6, no. 1, p. 18.

98 One such epiphyte, *Miltonia clowesii*, successfully raised and flowered on a piece of wood, was illustrated in *The Magazine of Botany* [ed: Joseph Paxton] in 1842.

99 Now named *Gongorra galeata* (syn. *Maxillaria galeata*).

100 Now available as cultivars Alba, Delicata, Innocens, and Splendens (RHS Encyclopaedia of House Plants).

101 John Loudon [ed.], 'Calls at London Nurseries: The Hackney Botanic Garden' *The Gardener's Magazine*, (1833), vol. 9, p. 467.

102 'The Late Mr. George Loddiges' *Journal of the Horticultural Society,* Vol. 1, 1846, p. 224. The sale of these orchids was not only through Loddiges' catalogue but also by auction through Protheroe and Morris in Cheapside and Stevens in Covent Garden.

103 The largest orchid in the world is *Grammatophyllum speciosum*; an epiphytic orchid from Malaysia, Indonesia, Thailand and the Philippines. Some specimens grow to forty feet in diameter, others have been weighed at over a ton, or described as big enough to fill a Pickford's van. From a specimen collected in the late 1890s, a small piece reached Kew Gardens. However the first plants to flower in Britain did so half a century before – at Loddiges Nursery in 1852. Joyce Stewart, 'The Largest Orchid', *The Garden: Journal of the Royal Horticultural Society* (1993) Jan. issue, p. 8.

104 James Bateman moved to Biddulph Grange, Staffs in 1840. His garden there was laid out 1849–64 by George Loddiges' son-in-law Edward Cooke.

105 David Allen, *The Victorian Fern Craze* (1969).

106 Dr Joseph Priestley resided briefly in Hackney after being hounded out of the Midlands under Pitt's Reign of Terror, and prior to his emigration to America in 1795. In his autobiography Priestley commented 'I spent my time even more happily at Hackney than ever I had done before.' Priestley found particular pleasure through his friendship in Hackney with Theophilus Lindsey and his wife, with whom he co-founded Unitarianism. Dr Priestley ministered at the Old Gravel Pit Meeting House, a few minutes' walk from Loddiges Nursery.

107 'Improved Method of Transporting Living Plants' *Companion to The Botanical Magazine* (1836), vol.1, p. 317.

108 Lynn Barber, *The Heyday of Natural History* (1980), and Ray Desmond, *A Celebration of Flowers* (1987). A vast quantity of the Cinchona (quinine-producing) seed was sent to Kew from the plant's native Peru in doubtful legal circumstances. Joseph Hooker oversaw its germination and then the young plants were transported to India. This event is commemorated in a stained glass window

in St Anne's Church, Kew Green.

109 The first publication was 'Method of Conveying Ferns and Mosses from Foreign Countries and of Growing them with success in the Air of London' *Trans. Soc. Arts*, (1833–4), vol. 1, p. 225. Ward's paper was presented to the next years BA meeting and read in his absence by John Lindley.

110 Shirley Hibberd, *Rustic Adornments for House and Home* (1856), p. 133.

111 John Harvey, *Early Nurserymen* (1974). The Horticultural Society leased a site for its gardens at Chiswick where it began to develop an arboretum only in 1823. Joseph Paxton was employed here on a low wage before he was elevated to the status of Head Gardener at Chatsworth.

112 John Loudon [ed.], 'Calls at London Nurseries: The Hackney Botanic Garden' *The Gardener's Magazine*, (1833), vol. 9, p. 467.

113 Benjamin Clarke, (1893), *op. cit.*

114 Ibid.

115 John Loudon [ed.], *The Gardener's Magazine*, (1828); [This increased to '70–80' species and varieties by 1833 and in *Arboretum et Fruticetum Britannicum* (1838), vol. 2, p. 849, John Loudon noted that 'most of the collections of *Crataegus* not only in Britain but also on the Continent have been procured from the Hackney nursery'].

116 René Desfontaines (1750–1833) named the Mexican Hawthorn *C. loddigesiana* Desf. but it was not a widely accepted name. Its other early name was *C. mexicana*. Its current taxonomy is *C. pubescens* Steud (syn. *C. stipulaceae* Loudon). It is shrubby in cultivation in Europe except when grafted onto common hawthorn [refs: Alfred Rehder, *Manual of Cultivated Trees & Shrubs* (1967), p.365, and John Loudon [ed.], *The Gardener's Magazine*, (1833), vol. 9, 1833 p. 630].

117 John Loudon [ed.], 'Calls at London Nurseries: The Hackney Botanic Garden', *The Gardener's Magazine*, (1833) vol. 9, p.467.

118 i.e. 1834

119 [notice of death of C.L.], *The Gardener's Magazine*, (1826), vol. 1, p. 229.

120 Many are said to have been made close to London, either at the Duke of Northumberland's famous tree collection at Syon or at Loddiges' Hackney Botanic Garden (ref: Miles Hadfield Pioneers in Gardening, (n/d)).

121 The several artists whose illustrations were engraved for the plates, included George Loddiges, Miss Jane Loddiges, George Cooke, Edward Cooke, William Cooke, T. Boys, Miss Rebello and W. Miller. Edward Cooke's diaries indicate that George Loddiges drew 889, and Edward Cooke 410, but note that other figures are given elsewhere for the number drawn by George Loddiges e.g. *J.Hort. Soc.* (1846), vol. 1, p. 224. Where the plates are individually attributed an enumeration can be made.

122 However Anon (1846) claims that 1,700 of the 2,000 plates were drawn by Mr Loddiges.

123 Quote by W.B.Hemsley in Wilfred Blunt, *The Art of Botanical Illustration* (1950), p. 212.

124 Letter to J. Sims 16 April 1817 [at Royal Botanic Gardens, Kew Archive].

125 (letter by John W. Ford), *Athenaeum*, (1899), 11 March, p. 311.

126 *The Botanical Cabinet*, (1817–34) (There are various mentions in secondary sources such as J. Bretschneider, *History of European Botanical Discoveries in China* (1898), vol. 1, p. 281, and C. Brickell, *The Vanishing Garden* (1986)).

127 H.R. Fletcher, *The Story of the Royal Horticultural Society* (1969) p. 93.

128 John Loudon [ed.], 'Calls at London Nurseries: the Hackney Botanic Garden' *The Gardener's Magazine*, (1833) vol. 9, p. 467.

129 Sources of information on Bartram's seeds sent to Loddiges include *The Botanical Cabinet* (1817–34); John Loudon, *Arboretum et Fruticetum Britannicum*

(1838), vol. 1, p. 84, Ray Desmond, *A Celebration of Flowers* (1977) ; H. Fletcher, *The Story of the Royal Horticultural Society* 1804–1968 (1969), p. 11.

130 'Journal Kept by David Douglas During his Travels in North America 1823–1827', *Trans. Royal Hort. Soc.*, (1914), p. 25.

131 John Loudon, *Arboretum et Fruticetum Britannicum* (1838), vol. 1, p. 84. The species included *Morus tatarica*, *Cornus ciscinata*, *Genista sibirica* and *Rhododendron chamaecistu*.

132 Inwards Books/Kew Record Books (1793–1809 p. 222, & p. 248/9 & p. 250/1/2/3; 1804–26 p. 192, p. 232) Royal Botanic Gardens, Kew.

133 'Catalogue of Plants Purchased of Loddiges & Sons, Hackney for His Majesty's Botanic Garden, Kew by Mr Aiton April 3rd 1806' Inwards Books/Kew Record Books Royal Botanic Gardens, Kew Archive.

134 Unfortunately this tree/shrub has not survived at Kew. The modern name is as per ref: W.J. Bean, *Trees and Shrubs Hardy in the British Isles* (1970–3). Most of the purchases from Loddiges Nursery, as recorded by the inwards books, were made between 1802–8, although palms were bought in 1826.

135 Director's Correspondence (letters to William J Hooker) 6 July 1841 Royal Botanic Gardens, Kew Archive. The first plants collected by Mr Smith came as a consignment of orchids.

136 'The Trial of Robert Sweet at the Old Bailey before Mr Justice Best' Tracts 1070, (1824) [British Library], and E.J.Wilson, 'West London Nursery Gardens' (Fulham and Hammersmith Historical Society 1982). Wilson writes that it was 'Konrad Loddiges' (sic) who gave the character evidence.

137 Jacob Rintz, 'Remarks on Various Gardens around London', *Gardener's Magazine*, (1829), vol. 5, p. 379.

138 Professor Sir William Jackson Hooker and his successor at Kew, his son Sir Joseph Dalton Hooker (1817–1911) are buried at St Anne's Church, Kew Green. They have additional memorials inside the church, inset with 'Wedgewood Blue'

139 Charles Knight, London, (1851), vol. 5, p. 315.

140 The Juliusspital Archive contains the original order details.

141 'Hortus Ericacaeus Woburnensis'.

142 *The Botanical Cabinet*, (1825), vol. 11, plate 1027.

143 Noel Kingsbury, 'Fashion Under Glass' *The Garden*, (1991), p. 298; and H. Fletcher, (1969), *op.cit.*, p. 11.

144 Visits by the Duke of Devonshire were frequent [ref: Benjamin Clarke, (1893), *op. cit.*, p. 39], and George Chadwick, *The Works of Sir Joseph Paxton 1803–1865*, (1961), p. 22.

145 John Loudon [ed.], 'Calls at London Nurseries: the Hackney Botanic Garden', *The Gardener's Magazine*, vol. 9, 1833, p. 467.

146 John Loudon [ed.], *The Gardener's Magazine*, (1843).

147 John Loudon [ed.], 'Abney Park Cemetery', *The Gardener's Magazine*, vol. 19, 1843.

148 John Loudon, *On the Laying-out, Planting & Managing of Cemeteries* (1843), p. 22.

149 John Loudon, *Arboretum et Fruticetum Britannicum*, (1838), p. 1557.

150 George Loddiges' election to Fellow of the Linnean Society is dated 5 Dec 1820. His proposers included Joseph Sabine, Edward Forster, and John Lindley. He was a Council Member of the Horticultural Society from 1820 until his death.

151 There is a reference to the site of the house in George Loddiges' will, proved 1846, (PRO.B/11/2040) which refers to it as a 'leasehold house in Paradise Fields'. It is shown on a number of local maps and the St Thomas' Hospital estate map.

152 Styled 'The Royal Microscopical Society' after 1866 by command of Queen Victoria.

153 Issued September 1989.

154 The invention of the achromatic lens is normally dated 1830.

155 'The President's Address: the history of the Royal Microscopical Society' *J. Royal Mic. Soc.* (1895), Feb. issue, pp. 1–21; a new history of the Society is being prepared by Professor Turner (pers. comm. 1988).

156 The Linnean Society of London has correspondence from George Loddiges in its Ward and Swainson collections. It has 11 letters written by George Loddiges to William Swainson concerning humming-birds [ref: the William Swainson Catalogue p. 44]. Correspondence about humming-birds written to Henry Doubleday is in the Passmore Edwards Museum, Newham.

157 *Loddigesia mirabilis* and *Cephalepsis loddigesi* Gould. The former was found in Peru in the 1840s; Loddiges' specimen was the only one known until 1880.

158 'The Late Mr George Loddiges' *J. Hort. Soc.*, (1846) vol. 1, p. 224.

159 Ibid. George Loddiges was an expert taxidermist who set most of the birds up himself. His views on taxonomy – e.g. that tails and bills were not an appropriate basis for classification – were communicated to Swainson [Linnean Society, Swainson Correspondence 20/4/1831].

160 Isabella Tree, *The Ruling Passion of John Gould: a biography of the bird man* (1991), p. 158.

161 'The Late Mr George Loddiges', *J. Hort. Soc.*, (1846) vol. 1. p. 224, and Linnean Society, Swainson Correspondence [letter by George Loddiges to Swainson 17 Nov 1827].

162 Isabella Tree, *op.cit.*, pp. 158–62;, and Maureen Lambourne, *John Gould – the Bird Man* (1982).

163 q.v. Isabella Tree, *op.cit.*, pp. 158 and 234.

164 A. Rutgers, *Birds of South America* (1972), (Marvellous Spatuletail plate/notes p. 313) and Loddiges' Plover-crest (plate/notes p. 221).

165 It had been named between 1830 and 1835.

166 Obituaries: *Proc. Linn. Soc.*, (1847), p. 334 and *J. Hort. Soc.*, (1846), p. 224.

167 The Agricultural Association certificate is deposited at Hackney Archives Department D/F/LOD 4.

168 See Benjamin Clarke, *op.cit.*, p. 297, note 129.

169 Isobel Watson, *Gentlemen in the Building Line: the development of South Hackney* (1989), pp. 70 & 74.

170 Conrad's decision is communicated 16/Jan/1850 in a letter to Joseph Jackson Hooker [ref: Director's Correspondence, Royal Botanic Gardens Library, Kew].

171 Ibid.

172 Eliza (38), though American-born was a UK citizen.

173 Mavis Batey, 'Edward Cooke, Landscape Gardener: a Victorian par excellence', *Garden History*, vol. 6, no. 1, p. 18. [ref: Edward Cooke's diary entry for 24/4/51].

174 Loddiges' hardy conifers were potted up and sold at 38 King St, Covent Garden three days after the auction advert [ref: Peter Hayden, *Biddulph Grange, Staffordshire: a Victorian garden rediscovered* (1989), p. 132].

175 Sale of all remaining stock to Sir Joseph Paxton [ref: *Gardener's Chronicle*, (1852), 8 Sept. p. 616]. Joseph Paxton was knighted in 1851.

176 'Removal of a Gigantic Palm-tree', *Illustrated London News* (1854), 5 Aug, p. 11. See also letter by T. Younghusband of Gerards-hall-inn, 23 Old Bailey, in *The Times*, (1854), July 28.

177 The palm itself weighed one ton and was 50ft tall. Latan Palms (fan palms) are tropical. One species is now called *Latania loddigesii* after Loddiges. Using current plant taxonomy it is still unclear precisely which species was transferred to the

Crystal Palace. It may have been The Blue Latan Palm (Mauritius Island only), the Red Latan Palm (Réunion Is., Mascarene Islands), or Yellow Latan Palm (Rodriguez Is., Mascarene Islands). All three are now Endangered Species.

178 Acquired from the Palace by Mr Thomas Evans of Stepney, upon whose death in 1814 it was bought by Loddiges Nursery.

179 The Crystal Palace opened in 1854.

180 1856 is sometimes given as the date of closure of the Nursery but supporting evidence is not yet available. Henry Curry's work is described briefly in Isobel Watson, *op. cit.*

181 Benjamin Clarke, (1893) *op.cit.*, describes the house as sited where the pub was built on Paragon/Frampton Park Road corner (see Godfrey Edition OS reprint 'Hackney 1893' or '1913'). This is correct although as much of the house and yard lies under Frampton Park Road itself where it joins Paragon Road.

182 For the dedication of roads see J/BW/E/13/2 Hackney Archives Department. The nineteenth-century building development on the nursery site is well shown on the 1894–6 O/S map (5ft to one mile scale) which shows individual house and garden shapes and greenhouses.

183 Certificate deposited at Hackney Archives Department D/F/LOD 5.

184 The Spurstowe Charity originated from his will (under which almshouses were built), receiving a regular income from the rents of two fields contributed by his brother. The almshouses, numbers 1–11 Silvester Path, were demolished in 1966. Details concerning the Spurstowe Charity can be found in Benjamin Clarke (1893) *op.cit.*, p. 65 (and additional notes by David Mander p. 289 of 1986 reprint), also M201 in Hackney Archives Department for Conrad's land exchange 12.5.1862.

185 Benjamin Clarke (1893) *op.cit.*, p. 38.

186 William Robinson, *Athenaeum*, (1899), 18 Feb. p. 214. The auction was held on 23 March 1899 by auctioneers Puttick & Simpson (now part of Phillips), but no records of the sale remain.

187 22 January 1988, aged 85 years.

188 The auction took place at Sotheby's on 24 June 1988 as lots 193 and 194 (Sotheby's Catalogue p. 97). *The Botanical Cabinet* sold for £9,500. The 150 water-colours had not been published as engravings in *The Botanical Cabinet* and sold for £2,800. Both were sold to Walford.

189 George Cooke's father was from Frankfurt-am-Main.

190 Director's Correspondence, Royal Botanic Gardens, Kew [Archive]. Black-edged letter to Hooker from George Loddiges 2 Feb 1844.

191 Each delivery of plants was noted in Edward Cooke's diary e.g. 'John Dent came with a load of plants from Mr Loddiges consisting of tall trees for Shrubbery and some American plants.'

192 Bateman acquired Biddulph Grange in 1840 and commissioned Cooke to work on its landscaping between 1849 and 1864.

193 Benjamin Clarke (1893) *op.cit.*, p. 39.